LECTURES IN MEDICAL PSYCHOLOGY

An Introduction to the Care of Patients

LECTURES IN MEDICAL PSYCHOLOGY

An Introduction to the Care of Patients

GRETE L. BIBRING, M.D.
and
RALPH J. KAHANA, M.D.

INTERNATIONAL UNIVERSITIES PRESS, INC.
NEW YORK

Manufactured in the United States of America

""Αξιοσ ὠφελεῖν τοὺσ ἀλγοῦντασ."

Worthy to serve the suffering

α ω α

Preface

A few words need to be said about the history of these lectures. They were first given in 1946, when I was appointed Head of the Department of Psychiatry at the Beth Israel Hospital in Boston, Mass. and Associate in Psychiatry at the Harvard Medical School to teach psychiatry as it applies to medicine.

At that time I was struck by the great need of all those who took care of patients with physical illnesses—doctors, nurses, dietitians, social workers, house staff—to include the patient's psychological structure and emotional conflicts in their management. These conflicts are inseparable from physical illness, which inevitably creates feelings of anxiety, depression, and helplessness in all human beings. Yet, at that time, these factors were taken into consideration only when they presented an insurmountable obstacle to the medical treatment of patients.

As a psychoanalyst, I felt that I could provide doctors with a general framework that would permit them to deal knowledgeably with all sorts of problems presented by medical patients. While the emotional conflicts and stresses posed by physical illness are universal, psychoanalysis teaches us how each individual deals with them in unique ways that are rooted in the history of his development.

In the beginning I presented formal lectures in amphitheaters, followed by question and discussion periods. These were combined with teaching rounds on the hospital wards, where patients were interviewed. My aim was to develop, with the help of clinical material and the theoretical framework of psychoanalytic psychology, a program of comprehensive medicine.

Over the years, until I retired in 1965 as Clinical Professor of Psychiatry at Harvard University, Faculty of Medicine, and Psychiatrist-in-Chief at the Beth Israel Hospital, these lectures were given, in various forms, to the students at the Harvard Medical School and the physicians—surgeons, pediatricians, internists, obstetricians, and psychiatrists—psychologists, social workers, nurses, and dietitians at the Beth Israel Hospital.

During this period I received many requests to publish them, but I hesitated for a number of reasons. There is a difference between addressing a live audience to whom the lecturer can actively respond and writing for a wide and invisible audience with great variations in training. Throughout my teaching it was possible to supplement and enrich the lectures according to the needs of the audience and in close contact with the clinical material the nurses and doctors were coping with at the moment. But this cannot be done as effectively in written reports. Another source of my hesitation was my awareness that for the sake of clear and useful outlines any claim to completeness of the topics presented had to be waived as well as any discussion and elaboration of specialized interests.

That this book nevertheless appears in print is due primarily to the persuasive and patient insistence and help of Dr. Ralph J. Kahana, one of my associates and coworkers for many years. I wish to take this opportunity to express my sincere thanks to Dr. Kahana for his assistance. Together we undertook the task of selecting, combining, and integrating these lectures, while retaining as far as possible their original form.

The lectures start with psychodynamic concepts that link together specific observations of behavior. They attempt to indicate how these concepts evolved and to discuss their place among psychoanalytic and other scientific theories. They follow the course of individual personality development throughout life, examining, at each step, the ensuing implications for the care of medical and surgical patients. The formative childhood years and the most critical periods of life, such as puberty, pregnancy, and aging, are given special attention. "Medical psychotherapy" is discussed more fully in a final, summarizing section.

In addition to the main bibliography, we have made specific suggestions for further reading at the end of each lecture, including both original sources and expositions that provide more complete or advanced treatment of topics, present different viewpoints, or introduce further applications and related areas of knowledge. Supplementing the principal focus of these lectures—the healthy personality of the adult as he adapts to the stresses of illness—references are given to pediatric psychiatry, psychosomatic processes, and psychopathological disorders.

Under the best of circumstances any introduction to this field must meet with a mixed reception. Students or even experienced professionals who are very perceptive and empathic in their responses to their own family members and friends can, nevertheless, be quite reluctant and overcautious when they are confronted with the emotional reactions of their patients. Some find it awkward to re-examine and amplify their personal psychological approach, which they have developed and used without special reflection. We therefore anticipate that some of our readers will feel that they have learned little that they did not know, while others will fear that they are being asked to acquire a totally new way of meeting, understanding, and dealing with people. Unavoidably, some readers will find portions of the material to be too unsophisticated, others too esoteric.

Yet in our selection we were guided by the type of teaching material that has been found most useful by the various groups of students and doctors who have been studying with us. The lectures reflect our conviction that those who work to alleviate and cure illness and promote and sustain health need a deeper understanding of the individuals they treat. This understanding always begins with a genuine, realistic concern and sympathy for the patient which then can be enhanced greatly by a systematic framework of pertinent psychological factors. Since the potential of knowledge and experience in this field is virtually limitless, we shall be content if our introduction to comprehensive medicine can set forth some basic principles, illustrate the sources and characteristic applications of these general propositions, and stimulate further learning.

Grete L. Bibring, M.D.

Cambridge, Mass., 1968

Acknowledgments

While the bulk of the case material stems from the senior author's clinical experience, additional case material was borrowed from other members of the staff or from outside sources whenever it seemed helpful. I take this opportunity to thank Dr. Ralph J. Kahana, Dr. Arthur R. Kravitz, and Dr. Robert L. Pyles from our Psychiatric Service, Dr. Benson R. Snyder of the Psychiatric Service of the Massachusetts Institute of Technology, Miss Berta Bornstein, child psychoanalyst in New York City, and Professor O. Hobart Mowrer of the University of Illinois, for permission to use their material.

We also wish to thank E. P. Dutton and Co. for permission to reprint the selection from the book *When We Were Very Young* by A. A. Milne, and New Directions Publishing Corp. for permission to reprint the selection from the book *Safe Conduct* by Boris Pasternak.

Mrs. Miriam Winkeller has earned our appreciation for her flawless typing of the lectures, revisions, and final manuscripts.

The person who added considerably to this effort was our knowledgeable and most helpful editor, Lottie M. Newman, whose questions and suggestions we valued highly.

Our profound gratitude goes to the superb medical staff of the Beth Israel Hospital—the psychiatric as well as the non-psychiatric—and to the members of the allied professions that make up its unique population with their thoughtful, stimulating devotion to acquiring any knowledge that will help in their service to the patient.

Last but not least, we want to thank our medical students who, with their intelligent and provocative inquiry into vague and fuzzy corners of our science, made it mandatory for all of us to arrive at the clearest possible definitions and to delineate as carefully as we could what we believe we know and what we only wish we knew.

Contents

xiii

Part III

Puberty and Adolescence

Part IV

Adult Life

Part V

Medical Psychotherapy

Part I

INTRODUCTION

Adaptation, Adjustment and Personality

At a certain point in our medical studies our knowledge of morphology or chemistry does not suffice any longer. This is when we meet the living patient, not as physiologists or histologists but as doctors. We no longer deal with a test tube, a microscopic slide, or even with a clinical syndrome alone, but with a person who is involved, who reacts emotionally and is in need of our help. We can give this help fully only if we are in command of a great deal of factual medical knowledge and of something else—a genuine understanding of the individual with whom we have to work. As physicians we constantly deal with the different conflicts, solutions, and personality traits of our patients. We may find signs of their maladjustment in the neuroses and are faced with the disintegration of their adaptive efforts in the psychoses. The doctor has to learn that there are critical phases in the life cycle of individuals which tax their equilibrium: puberty, pregnancy, and aging are outstanding examples of these. Individual situations like the loss of love objects, personal and professional failures, diseases and the like will assume traumatic importance. General stress situations, of which wars or disasters are extreme representatives, become the pathogenic events and we will have to consider them when evaluating each patient's entire condition, his psychological or psychosomatic tolerance and his need for support or protection.

Psychological conditions are not static and cannot be truly studied and comprehended in an isolated state; they are always an intrinsic part of the whole personality, have always to be judged within this framework, and are the result of each person's entire history. It is essential in the psychological appraisal to remain mindful that everything observed may be significant as an expression of a variety of underlying matters. For example, if we consider a patient's "courage" in the presence of a serious illness, we cannot draw any final conclusion from what seems courageous in this behavior as long as we look upon it as a phenomenon isolated from the rest of his personality. Only by judging it in its proper context can we determine whether this is courage growing out of strength and reasoning, or whether it is the rigid denial of a mounting anxiety, or the result of an effort in a patient who is ashamed of appearing weak, or a way of shaking off the overprotective concern of a possessive, controlling family, or whether this "courage" stems from a limited understanding and thus unawareness of the danger. Each of these underlying meanings represents a distinct psychological configuration and requires a different approach by the skillful doctor.

In order to establish a more adequate understanding of human behavior we will have to outline and discuss personality aspects as they develop in the history of the individual and as they enter into his present-day attitudes. This history has to be understood as a process of adjustment leading to changing patterns of behavior by which the growing individual achieves a certain harmony and equilibrium between himself and his environment. In other words, we shall attempt to follow in a general outline the individual's development under the influence of his environment, and the individual's adjustment to this environment. In doing this, we shall set forth at the same time the principles of psychoanalytic psychology and how this system has to be understood as the psychology that bridges not only the gap between the individual and his environment but also between the biological sciences on the one hand and the social sciences on the other. It is of interest to note that advances in endocrine research and our growing knowledge of psychosomatic relationships reconfirm the importance of a biological orientation in understanding adaptation. However, the expectation that with increasing knowledge of biological factors psychoanalytic psychology will become superfluous represents a basic fallacy. The comprehension of this specificity of reactions at the psychological level of integration of the organism may be enriched but cannot be superseded by biological data. On the other hand, most of the psychological systems that stem but diverge from psychoanalysis have in common the disregard of biological factors in psychological development and functioning.

In our presentation we shall follow the historical development of psychoanalytic concepts and trace how Freud, on the basis of his clinical observations, formulated, step by step, the role played by the instinctual conflicts and their solution toward environmental adjustment in the genesis of normal personality formation and of neuroses. Let us begin with a rough sketch, a model of the process through which the child in growing up reaches the stage of the mature, rational individual in a slow, painstaking process of adjustment to the world around him.

We have to assume that the infant is born as a predominantly instinctual being with primitive drives, and an Anlage or potential to higher, less impulse-directed functioning. All we can surmise is that there is active in him the urge to gratify his most vital, pressing needs. He has no clear knowledge and certainly has no experience of the outside world. He is at first without any emotional attachment or interest in the environment, and without any psychological or physical control over himself beyond ingestive and protective reflexes, and latent perceptual, intellectual, and motor capacities.

How can we understand the road from this initial state to the adult individual who has become a firmly established member of the family and community? The primitive, original drives in the infant, if they were left to themselves, might lead to more greed for satisfaction, to more self-centered and inconsiderate behavior as the child grows older and stronger. But the child's impulses constantly meet with the limitations, restrictions, and increasingly with the criticisms that stem from his environment. Here the first interactions take place. We assume, and we think that observations and investigations substantiate this assumption, that the child learns to control his impulses because of his dependence upon and his growing attachment to the first objects in his life, his parents. In order to preserve their affection and protection or to avoid their dissatisfaction and rejection, the child attempts his first steps toward adjustment to the world around him. As he grows older and wiser he learns to judge for himself what the grownups want him to do or not to do. He will not always need their direct admonition: "Don't do this" or "Be sure to be good." He will not even forever need their presence in order to try to behave well. He will gradually take over his parents' commands; i.e., he internalizes these directions and makes them his own, as part of his conscience. We may call his endeavor to live up to these requests within himself a second step toward adjustment.

Does the effort to control his undesirable impulses really change him inwardly? Will he stop wanting to be selfish, dirty, lazy, or engaged in forbidden things? Will he stop being viciously jealous of his brother or sister? To achieve this a third important step in this maturational process is taken. In his struggle to become a truly lovable child, a struggle which so soon changes from an outer to an inner one, no longer between himself and his parents but between his impulses and his conscience, the child has quite an array of methods at his disposal. We call these methods the *mechanisms of defense*. They are employed by the child in order

to ward off within himself those impulses which he has
learned to regard as objectionable, disgusting or shameful.
That is, in order to allay the anxiety that signals a threatening punishment or inner censure he will have to do more than
try to hold back the impulse and not act it out. He will
attempt to reject it so effectively that he loses sight of it and
becomes unaware of its existence within himself. One of the
most effective methods of achieving this, but also potentially
a most fateful one, is to repress. *Repression* is a decisive means
of excluding thoughts and feelings from the realm of our
conscious knowledge, but one that carries with it certain consequences:

The child is at this point "adjusted" to the requirements
of his parents. He not only behaves like a good child, but at
this point to all intents and purposes he has become a good
child.

Repression is effective only as far as the child's awareness is concerned, but it does not diminish the intensity of the
repressed impulse and conflict. They may remain within the
child cut off from entering consciousness, but also largely
precluded from being worked out or discharged and replaced
by other interests as it may happen in the normal process of
growing up. It is as if a door were closed on them, and this
door has to be kept shut with some persistent effort in order
to prevent the exiled wishes from breaking through. This
state of equilibrium often proves rather vulnerable.

If in the future, and this may be sooner or later, traumatic
experiences under unfavorable life conditions stir up these
repressed conflicts or weaken the repressive forces, this labile
adjustment may be upset. The impulse threatens to break
through and, as we shall try to demonstrate, this can lead to
neurotic symptoms. The neurotic symptom is a camouflaged,
disguised expression of the repressed impulse, which is not
recognizable in its true, unconscious meaning and is experienced by the patient as a strange, frightening or incomprehensible intrusion into his life.

In order to illustrate these concepts, we shall take a relatively simple example, choosing only the details of the case which will help us to demonstrate their meaning. Mr. A. who suffered from alcoholism came to a psychiatrist with the following story: until two years ago he had never drunk on any but social occasions, and then only moderately. At that time his wife had given birth to their first child, a little boy, fulfilling a great longing of his: he had always very much wanted to have children, but it had taken years before his wife became pregnant. He remembered that on the evening of her delivery, when he was told to leave the hospital because the child would not arrive before morning, he went for the first time alone to a bar since he felt too nervous and anxious to go home all by himself. There he took a few drinks just to relax.

In the following weeks after his wife and the baby returned from the hospital, his visits to the bar became more and more frequent, and took place between the close of his office hours and his arrival at home. Mr. A. knew that he didn't feel quite comfortable and at ease under the new family regime at home. Everything now centered around the child. His wife with whom he had shared everything before, who had insisted on his telling her first of all about what he had experienced during his working day, had little time left for this. All she did was to recount in detail what had gone on with the baby. Within a short period his drinking became excessive, but fortunately he kept enough insight and understanding to recognize the abnormal, compulsive, and pathological in his behavior, and to look for help.

This patient had, as a boy of four, a not unusual, but for him very traumatic experience. Until then he had been an only, very beloved child unusually close to his mother, especially because his father was a salesman, away on the road for long periods. At that time, "suddenly," a little baby brother came into his family. He reacted to this event with strong hostility and jealousy, became very angry and aggressive whenever he saw his mother nurse the child, and was severely punished for this behavior. For the first time tension developed between him and his mother. After a few weeks he showed a first and very informative symptom. He started sleepwalking, wandering through the house until he came to the room where his parents slept with the baby, and calling out, crying, while still asleep, "I want my cocoa, I want my cocoa." This complaint was probably a substitute for begging to be nursed by mother like the baby.

His parents were not very friendly with the little boy because of this incessant disturbance, and after a while they decided to lock him in his room at night. Nobody knows how and when it happened, but he gave up this symptom. For us this means that he did not necessarily lose, but he repressed his jealousy of and hostility to the baby. The arrival of his own infant son reawakened this old trauma of his childhood, buried long ago, and revived the unconscious envy and jealousy of those days. He feared losing his mother then, his wife now, to the little intruder; he now craved not for cocoa, but for alcohol. The deeper significance of this drink also remained the same as in childhood: to find comfort, and to prove that he too has to be considered and get his share of satisfaction or mother's love, even though he had to request it in a disguised, devious way.

Let us now take another example that might help us further along in our understanding: Jim, like most little boys at a certain phase of development, loves to torture small animals. He does all kinds of mean things to the cats of the neighborhood, sometimes even brutal things. There is no doubt that he enjoys this activity. His concentration upon it and his involvement indicate this clearly. At the same time he seems to know that the grownups dislike these little games and would scold or punish him for them if they found out. We as observers notice that this entertainment seems highly charged for him, that it is obviously exciting for the boy. We are inclined to classify it as a childhood equivalent of what we are used to call, in adults, sadistic impulses or acts. Now let us assume that Jim is severely frightened or punished for this behavior or that he went too far and inflicted great injury upon his own beloved kitten, with the result that he feels intensely guilty and remorseful. This represents a situation which frequently leads to the repression of the offensive sadistic impulses. If the repression is successful, he will not want to torture cats any longer. He has accepted the code of his group and adjusted to it. This could be a permanent solution and the end of the story.

Yet in the case of the child we have in mind with a similar history, the course of events was different. When Jim was sixteen years old he received his driver's license. Driving had a special meaning for him—to assert himself against his father's overconcern about the boy's "immaturity and clumsiness." On his first extensive trip alone he ran over a little cat. This is not a pleasant experience for anyone, especially if it happens on a first trip, and more so if it may confirm the low opinion father has of one. Normally one feels very badly about such an event, but after a while this can be worked off and one does not remain preoccupied with it. Not so with our young patient. Jim reacted far beyond what would ordinarily be the case. He became nauseated, almost fainted, and could not sleep comfortably for a while. Both when awake and in his anxious dreams he went over the events of the accident again and again. He developed headaches and fatigue that lasted for some time and he could not bring himself to resume driving. Following this he began to feel carsick when driven by somebody else. These symptoms spread even further; he slowly developed an intensive "phobia" against any kind of transportation, be it automobile, bus, or railway. He got into a panic when forced to travel and restricted his movements to distances he could cover on foot.

When you asked him at this point what this was all about, he could not answer—he hardly connected the onset of his phobia with the cat accident; but, as it was found in the careful study that followed, the basis of his disturbance went back to this accident and beyond it to strongly repressed sadistic childhood episodes of the nature that we described before. It was this adjustment through repression which had become upset and thrown out of balance by the later traumatic event. He reacted as if he had killed the little cat out of the same abhorrent impulse which had made him enjoy torturing animals as a child. His distress and guilt feeling over it were the unconscious reasons why he did not dare to drive a car again or even ride in a car which might strike another innocent victim.

We hope that we have made it clear that not every repression leads to neurosis. Repression is one of the most commonly employed means of dealing with inner conflicts in childhood and, as we pointed out before, a breakdown of the balance achieved by it will occur later on only under special conditions and constellations.

Repression is not the only way in which the child can deal with his inner conflicts. As mentioned, there are a variety of defenses at the child's disposal, all of which can serve the purpose of helping him adjust to his culture, fit into his family, and fight his objectionable tendencies in order to please his parents. When we inquire into the working of these defenses we can observe how in molding childhood impulses they have a most interesting and varied effect on personality development.

For example, the infantile sadistic impulse may become transformed in consequence of the struggle against it, attenuated in a complicated way, to a point where only faint traces of it remain as a personality tendency, a kind of merciless or aggressive lack of concern toward the world in general or toward helpless, weaker individuals in particular. This may be an unpleasant attitude in an individual, but would still pass as acceptable compared with unbridled sadistic acts.

The childhood tendency may be altered even more and changed to something rather constructive, leading to valuable achievement. Thus the boy's original interest in animals and their suffering could finally lead to his choice of becoming a veterinarian. We call this *sublimation*, i.e., using an initially unacceptable impulse for something socially valued by changing its goal; the initial impulse was to hurt animals and to seek excitement and some gratification through this activity; the sublimated goal is to attend their suffering only in order to help them, to cure them, to alleviate their pain, and to hurt them only if it cannot be avoided, with no conscious sadistic pleasure attached to it.

Out of the early struggle against this forbidden pleasure the child may develop a special kindness and tender concern for animals, protecting them overanxiously from any harm that may be done to them—and later in life become excessively involved in movements to prevent sadistic acts wherever they may be found. We use for this the term *reaction formation*, i.e., in order to fight objectionable impulses we call up the exactly opposite forces in us, so to speak, leaning over backward. This whole reaction formation may be *displaced* or shifted from animals onto people and generalized. A person reacting in this way may devote himself to the cause of anyone or anything that seems weak and oppressed. He may become a benefactor of "lame ducks" and a protector of the "underdog." Finally, he may develop as a reaction against these impulses a dislike of animals or an intolerance to their presence.

Instead of pursuing these themes further, we may now return to our original statement: at the beginning we said that psychoanalytic psychology and psychiatry represent an attempt to bridge the gap between the biological sciences and the social sciences; we can now say more explicitly: between the sciences concerned with the instinctual drives of the individual and those disciplines related to the demands of the environment in its social, cultural, and economic aspects. With regard to the instinctual drives, in psychoanalysis we assume two basic biological urges, on the one hand the aggressive drives which are predominantly in the service of self-preservation, and which attack whatever threatens or limits the security and well-being of the individual; and, on the other hand, those drives which pertain to the preservation of the species, that is, the sexual drives whose main aim is to love and to be loved, culminating in sexual union and procreation. Making this assumption, we can then say that the combinations and variations of the sexual and aggressive drives, including their infantile components, represent instinctual elements which are innate in the child. In studying the development of the child, we can observe the interaction between the derivatives of these drives and the pressures of the environment, as well as the resulting adjustment. Childhood development may be envisioned as a series of changes, of successive solutions to conflicts which lead to established modes of adjustment characteristic of each individual in adult life.

These persistent ways of coping with inner tensions and with the conditions of the world in which the person lives become established as essential elements of his personality. Terms such as soul, spirit, and character have been in use in the course of history to designate these resulting traits according to prevailing viewpoints. The theories of personality have a long and at times violently debated record. For centuries they fell into the realm of philosophy, and they continue to lend themselves to elaboration on the basis of value systems or ethics. Sometimes they were the creation of the scientific genius of a single individual. At other times they were included in what prevailed as the general theory of the laws of nature.

Aristotle, for example, taught that soul and body are one, that there is a differentiation of the soul into the vegetative soul (which included functions now related to the autonomic nervous system), the sensitive soul (including sensation, perception, feeling, and desire), and the intellectual soul (capable of the highest cognitive differentiations). With regard to the development of personality Socrates maintained that man is the result of his original nature and of society's influence on it: conventions, not the nature of man, are responsible for his customs.

With the growing significance of the church, moral and religious values entered into these theories and influenced them significantly. St. Thomas Aquinas attempted to blend the Aristotelian idea of the three kinds of souls as one with the body with theological concepts. He contrasted the intellectual soul as the immortal element with the lower, mortal aspects of soul and body. From then on through the middle ages all concern and thought centered around this immortal soul, and people completely lost the remainder of their personalities, so to speak.

Finally, in the Italian Renaissance, the "person" emerged again as a worldly type with individual characteristics. Special emphasis was placed on strength, courage, and leadership (the Condottieri), and the literature of that time is full of figures of intense, individualistic, overpowering drive. Spinoza's philosophy introduced the ethical man as the idealized leading type. The pedantic, self-disciplined, financially successful trader was put forward by the middle class emerging after the French Revolution. In a reaction to this the nineteenth century produced the image of the subtle, romantic hero with consuming, beautiful passions. These all represented models in the history of personality studies.

During the nineteenth century very important events took place in the world of science. Darwin's theory of evolution prepared the way for a completely new direction in the study of man. The significance of the developmental process now became a cornerstone of biology and psychology. The fact that man is part of the animal kingdom and not a detached spirit awakened interest in the instincts of man. This was elaborated especially by McDougall (1908). The significance of the developmental factors in the psychological maturational process of the child became a basic concept in Stanley Hall's work. Today's theories of personality combine the findings of the biological sciences of the nineteenth and the social sciences of the twentieth centuries. Man is seen as a biological and social being, a view that raises the question of what in man is conditioned by his biology and what by the influence of and interaction with his environment. All of today's personality theories have certain central principles in common:

1. The developmental point of view;
2. The concept of the mind-body unit (as inseparable);
3. The understanding that pathological personality formations are not alien inclusions but are to be understood as a deviant development of normal factors.

As far as their relations to biology and the social sciences are concerned, today's systems represent a complimentary series with the somatic typologists at one end and the so-called "neo-Freudians" at the other. Sheldon exemplifies the former and sees personality as determined by body habitus, leading to a classification of endomorphic, mesomorphic, and ectomorphic types. Karen Horney (1937) is a representative of the latter group, viewing personality almost exclusively as the reflection of environmental behavior. As indicated, the psychoanalytic theory of personality holds a middle position. Psychoanalysis has further specified the concepts of the environment and the biological constituents of personality as follows: environment is not only "society" in the abstract but is made up of specific people in the life of the individual. Internal factors are not only drives but the entire psychic apparatus. According to this theory, the psychic apparatus has to be understood in terms of three different, often conflicting forces within the individual.

The first, representing the instinctual drives, is named the *id*.

The second, representing the precipitate within the personality of the important environmental, social, and cultural laws, traditions, and ethical norms, thus including the functions of conscience, is called the *superego* or *ego ideal*. Its formation is initiated in the child through imitation of and identification with the parents because of his admiration for them and what they stand for, and because of his fear of them which contributes to his desire to obey.

The third agency postulated by this theory is a most interesting one in this context. It is the organizing agent within the personality, mediating between instincts, outside reality, and conscience or superego, integrating and balancing, and is instrumental in warding off what seems inappropriate in a given situation or accepting whatever is feasible of those opposing pressures. This core of the personality is called the *ego*. To define the ego more clearly: it is the facet or aspect or organization within the psychological structure which in a constant developmental process from infancy on represents the growing regulative and adaptive facilities. Its functions include the faculty to observe, to perceive the world around us and within us, to think, to test reality, to defend against anxiety, and to organize and direct action. We ascribe to it our innate abilities and talents, including our intellectual and artistic endowment. We can understand that these functions representing reason and reality in us are essential for our inner equilibrium and our adjustment. But we also have to appreciate that this central position cannot be maintained without constant effort and that the ego organization must often deal with quite strenuous tasks which are not always solved too well: sometimes we cannot keep down objectionable impulses; sometimes we have to defend our position too rigidly against them, at the expense of our own flexibility and free functioning; sometimes we submit too far to the severity of our superego and carry its colors too righteously. In the course of a lifetime the ego may come to show all kinds of battle scars which in turn indicate, often significantly, what the struggle was about.

As we go on to consider psychological development in detail, we shall see how the ego may, in spite of the effort to ward off, reject, and mold instinctual impulses, be invaded by them in disguised and attenuated form so that they become part of the personality characteristics. In real life the trends that we shall describe are often quite subtle and may enhance the personality more than disfigure it. Before proceeding to take up the course of this process in a systematic way, we think it will be helpful to discuss certain fundamental questions touching upon our basic approach and theory.

Psychoanalytic Psychology as a Science

> ". . . the scientist has no other method
> than doing his damnedest."
> P. W. Bridgman

Our effort to understand adaptive behavior has led us to begin with the consideration of the biological human drives in their earliest, infantile forms and in their later, modified manifestations. This is, by the way, an aspect of psychoanalytic theory about which people have often been critical: they found it hard to understand the significance of Freud's effort to remove psychological theories from the speculation of idealistic philosophy and to relate them to the biological substratum instead.

It is obviously difficult for all of us at first to see highly appreciated human qualities linked up with instincts which we are used to calling "primitive" or even "low." The difficulty is in part a result of the adult's need to defend himself against his primitive urges; in the interest of achieving control we tend to deny the importance of these instinctual wishes. This has in the past contributed to the inclination to disregard the unmistakable forerunners of adult sexual behavior which appear in childhood. As we learn to understand the deeper connections between well-organized, mature personality traits and primitive infantile tendencies, we also have to acquire a greater scientific objectivity toward these findings. The fact that these connections exist does not depreciate the cultural, aesthetic, or moral values of our adjustive achievements.

Another characteristic prejudice stemmed from the novelty of psychoanalytic conclusions, which seemed at variance with academic psychology and common, everyday experience. Psychology, in contrast to organic medicine or mathematics, is a field in which every human feels "at home" because he is aware of his own emotions and problems and those of others as he deals with them. A child who wants a new toy may already have learned to evaluate the atmosphere, how he has to go about it, when he may ask his parents, and so forth. In this way we all have grown up as psychologists, constantly endeavoring to understand others and ourselves. Then we are suddenly confronted by psychoanalysts who reinterpret our impressions of other people's psychological states or even amend what we think we know about ourselves. They use as their basis seemingly insignificant data, slips of the tongue, slight discrepancies between our statements and our facial expressions, the sequence of thoughts in "free association" and even dreams and other vague material. Thus it may easily seem that the psychoanalyst's propositions are arbitrary and unscientific.

If an educated person who was not a physicist had heard Max Planck, the originator of the quantum theory, state publicly that black bodies send out light, the listener might have thought that it sounded absurd and paradoxical. But as Planck was a physicist, the listener would give him credit and would have asked at the utmost how he arrived at this conclusion. Can he explain it? And Planck might have first discussed the normal spectrum, then what he called the cavity radiation spectrum, and then developed his theory. Similar questions have to be asked when evaluating modern psychoanalytic psychiatry as to its position as a science.

In order to set up a frame of reference for these questions, let us briefly review the fundamentals of empirical science in general and how they apply to psychoanalytic psychology. As we know, the first step in these sciences is observing and collecting phenomenological and descriptive data. Then we classify the data according to certain principles (like similarity, temporal concurrence, etc.). The most essential step in the scientific process is to explain the described and classified phenomena in a generally applicable form through constructs or hypotheses. This method, starting with empirical data and leading to explanatory constructs, is the inductive method.

We always will keep in mind that the hypothesis itself cannot be proved by direct observation as it is an explanation of the observed data, but it can be tested and may be verified by applying it to new observed data: as long as the hypothesis is helpful in explaining these, it is considered a valid theory. In fact, the hypothesis may be valuable because it suggests new areas of inquiry, and relates new findings to known phenomena in a comprehensive way (Kaplan, 1964).

However, if it happens that new observations cannot be explained by it, two things have to be considered; the theory has to be abandoned and replaced by one that can explain the new as well as the old data, or the theory has to be modified and supplemented. The credibility of the theory is enhanced if it can serve as the basis for successful predictions. There are other ways of testing the validity of a theory: one of them is verification by experiments—where the experiment can permit more accurate and detailed observations under varied conditions, and may help to decide which one of various alternative explanations is more satisfactory.

How do these scientific requirements apply to psychoanalytic psychology? A clearer awareness of the nature of its theoretical structure and of the possibility of validating its data may be gained by tracing the steps in which psychoanalysis developed.

Through the centuries people were concerned with psychological phenomena, expressed mainly in religion, superstition, and myths. Psychopathological conditions were believed to be caused by the spirits of the dead, the evil eye, demoniacal possession or the breaking of taboos. Although Hippocratic medicine made a beginning in the careful observation of mental disorders, this came to a standstill with the decline of classical science in the middle ages. Ideas of demoniacal possession and witchcraft returned and prevailed in medieval times, reaching a peak in the fifteenth century (Zilboorg and Henry, 1941). Reinstatement of the clinical method, the start of a more consistently humane approach to the mentally ill, and the beginning of modern psychology, came into being in the Renaissance.

One of the first attempts to approach psychiatric patients with a scientific hypothesis in terms of natural sciences, and a very faulty one according to our present state of knowledge, was made in the second half of the eighteenth century by a Viennese doctor, Franz Anton Mesmer (1733-1815). Before taking up medicine, Mesmer had attained doctorates in Divinity, Philosophy, and Law, and had written his Philosophy thesis on the effect of celestial bodies on the life of humans, a subject of widespread speculation in his time (Zweig, 1932). He thought that the influences of planets and stars upon mankind might be mediated through a "universal fluid." In 1774, Mesmer learned that one of his friends, the Jesuit Father Maximilian Hell, who was a physicist and astronomer, had been asked to prepare a magnet for purposes of healing. The notion of the curative powers of magnetic iron was an ancient one, connected with the belief that it came from meteorites and somehow "remembered" its origin by pointing to a star when used as a compass. Mesmer conceived the idea that magnetic energy might be the universal fluid and developed the theory that certain illnesses, which we today would diagnose as hysteria, were the results of the faulty distribution of magnetism in these patients. He very logically and systematically, therefore, set out to correct this disturbance by stroking his patients with a powerful magnet, to re-establish the correct arrangement of their magnetic structure. One of his patients was a Fräulein Maria Theresa Paradies, as famous a case in the history of psychiatry as was later Breuer and Freud's first patient, Anna O.

Fräulein Paradies, a gifted pianist and child prodigy, was the protégé of the Empress who paid for her education and gave her parents a pension. At the age of four, the girl had suddenly become blind with what was believed by the leading physicians to be an incurable disease of the optic nerves. Mesmer noted that she also had abdominal pain, a convulsive twitching of the eyes, and at times peculiar mental states, and he suspected that she had suffered some nervous shock and might respond to his therapy. He reported almost complete restoration of her sight, and this was substantiated in a detailed report by her father who recorded that at first Fräulein Paradies could bear only the light of a darkened room and perceive the outlines of objects; then she gradually began to distinguish hues of color, having to learn their names, and was puzzled by perspective. Interestingly, with the return of her vision, she began to develop fits of depression and found difficulties in playing pieces she had known by heart. In spite of this and other similar successes, or because of his success, Mesmer provoked the opposition of the Viennese medical profession to such a degree that they turned the all-powerful court and clergy against him. He escaped to Paris, and this event contributed significantly to the impressive development of psychiatry in France.

Within a year or two after he had begun treating patients by magnetism, Mesmer made the startling discovery that he could obtain the same therapeutic results without directly using a magnet. He had actively pursued his studies of "magnetic fluid" and had found that patients could be relieved of symptoms through contact with clothing, furniture, water, and even animals and a tree in his garden that had been exposed to magnets! Finally, the treatment came to be based solely upon the contact with the magnetiser or Mesmerist (as his followers were known) without the use of a magnet. Faced with these observations, Mesmer chose to modify his theory rather than abandon it. He ascribed the healing influence to the therapist's supposedly possessing healthy "animal magnetism," a subtler, analogous energy which reinforced and freed the flow of the patient's faulty magnetism. In 1843, an English surgeon, James Braid, studying the phenomena of Mesmerism, noted that the reactions and attitudes which the patient demonstrated showed definite similarity to the state of sleep. He concluded that the Mesmeric phenomena had nothing to do with magnetism and coined the term *hypnosis* from the Greek word *hypnos* for sleep. This therapeutic procedure remained for a long time the method of choice in treating hysterical neuroses.

In the latter part of the nineteenth century, the observation of hysterical patients under hypnosis was one of the special interests of Jean Martin Charcot at the Salpêtrière in Paris. He studied the so-called "accident hysterias" in which the illness followed a trauma such as a railway accident. He noticed that the patient's symptoms (e.g., paralysis, anesthesia, tremor, etc.) were ever so often clearly connected with the precipitating accident situation. This was remarkable because it never had been considered that these symptoms had an etiological relation to the rest of the patient's life experiences. Charcot furthermore discovered that the important factor was the specific idea of the accident rather than the physical trauma itself. For example, a patient in his anxiety during the accident may have been in terror of having his legs crushed. He then developed the fixed idea of having lost his legs, though no physical injury had occurred, with the result of hysterical paralysis and anesthesia of the legs. Charcot proceeded to experiment with hysterical patients by creating in hypnosis the illusion of an accident and then observed how the very same types of symptoms would be established, thus proving his theory that such disturbances resulted from the force of the idea and not from the physical impact of the trauma. As a scientist of that era he combined these new discoveries with one of the leading theories of the time and ascribed great etiological importance to heredity predisposing these patients to a "degenerated" nervous system. This led him to formulate the following theory of hysteria: in degenerated individuals characterized by exceptional states of consciousness, traumatic situations such as accidents create a narrowing of brain function which results in abnormal behavior, e.g., fixed ideas. Pierre Janet (1859-1947), a pupil of Charcot, modified this theory, replacing the concept of narrowing of brain function and fixed ideas by the construct of a splitting off or dissociation of thoughts from the rest of consciousness due to an inborn weakness in the capacity for psychic integration or synthesis.

In 1885, Sigmund Freud (1856-1939), whose main research had been in the field of neurology, came to Charcot to learn about hysteria. He came from the environment of a neurological laboratory headed by Brücke, Meynert, and Exner, leading figures of the "Helmholtz School of Physiology." Adherence to scientific method and the endeavor to explain the function of the organism in terms of physical and chemical factors were the hallmarks of this school, which had its influence on Freud's persistent efforts to develop a psychological system based upon biological foundations (Amacher, 1965). His special interest in the topic of hysteria had been stimulated by discussions with his friend, Dr. Josef Breuer, about one of Breuer's hysterical patients (Breuer and Freud, 1893-1895). The patient, Anna O., was an unusually intelligent, twenty-one-year-old girl who had developed a very severe mental disorder concurrently with her beloved father's terminal illness. Her symptoms included disturbances of speech, eye movements and vision, paralyzing contractures of her limbs, anesthesias, states of altered consciousness resembling sleepwalking or hypnotic trances, distaste for food, a nervous cough, mood changes between high spirits and anxious stubbornness, and frightening hallucinations of snakes. Breuer had noted that even in hypnosis the patient did not accept any suggestions which commanded improvement or disappearance of her symptoms. Such suggestions under hypnosis represented the then-established method of treatment. Nevertheless, Breuer had achieved a certain degree of therapeutic success through a different, unforeseen technique which developed in the course of his work with this patient.

He had observed that during her states of altered personality and confusion she often started to talk spontaneously, gradually telling in a very emotional way stories with a sad or disturbing content. After telling such a story, she would return to normal consciousness and be calm and comfortable for several hours. It turned out that these stories were based upon different experiences from her recent or remote past, experiences which she could not recollect when she was awake, and which in their content clearly showed a connection with her present symptoms. Whenever the patient told in hypnosis about the events which had occurred when one of her disabling impairments first arose, the symptom connected with this episode disappeared after she had awakened. For instance, at the time when a paralysis of her right arm had developed, the patient recalled in hypnosis the following scene: she remembered the time when her father was very ill, two years before, and she had nursed him through the whole period. She saw herself sitting by his bedside, completely exhausted, with her right arm over the back of the chair. In her anxiety not to disturb her father, who finally had fallen asleep, she did not dare to move that arm which had begun to feel quite stiff, numb, and painful from her sitting still like that. She described all the details and seemed to live through the whole painful emotion of that period, and when she awakened from hypnosis the hysterical palsy of her arm had disappeared. Anna O. aptly termed as "chimney sweeping" this procedure of bringing to light hidden memories and thus relieving her symptoms.

Breuer discussed these interesting phenomena with Freud, who thought that they were consistent with Charcot's viewpoint on hysterical symptoms: that they were not random afflictions in generally disturbed personalities, but seemed to have their specific meaning. Furthermore, he was impressed by the fact that this meaning did not seem accessible and comprehensible if the person was wide awake, but was attainable in a state of hypnosis, a condition which in itself posed a number of unanswered questions.

Thus in the year 1889 Freud went to Nancy in France to study hypnosis with Bernheim, the leading expert in that field. There he found in the posthypnotic order further evidence suggesting that powerful inner mental forces exist, hidden from the individual, and yet unmistakably affecting his behavior. For example, if we order a patient in hypnosis to perform a not too inappropriate act like opening a window and throwing out a glove five minutes or two days or a week after he wakes up, and if we add the suggestion that he will not remember receiving this order, he will comply on both counts. Five minutes or two days or a week later, in the midst of his occupation, he suddenly will appear somewhat absent-minded, a little peculiar in his behavior as if deeply in thought, and he will then open a window and throw out his glove. If he is asked for an explanation of this action, he will not know why he has done it, but will try to rationalize it somehow: he just wanted to make a joke, or he disliked the glove for a long time and tried to get rid of it. Only in hypnosis again or with great effort under the persuasion of the hypnotist without hypnosis, will he gradually remember the real events.

Freud combined all these impressions and arrived at a theoretical formulation that contradicted the general and exclusive viewpoint of his day. He inferred that in the individual there are psychological processes which affect him intensely though he is not aware of their existence. They are responsible for the formation of the hysterical symptom in the way that the hypnotic order is responsible for the formation of the person's curious posthypnotic behavior. He named these psychological elements *unconscious,* and this was one of the concepts that provoked the opposition of leading psychiatrists and the schools of academic psychology. The professions were not ready for the idea of anything psychological which was "unconscious"; and they were even less ready to ascribe so much power to such doubtful psychological factors.

These ingenious first steps which Freud and Breuer took in their research on hysteria remained the basic elements in what Freud termed psychoanalysis. In 1895 Breuer and Freud published their *Studies on Hysteria* and presented approximately the following formulation: in some individuals, extreme exhaustion leads to an exceptional state of mind in which they are incapable of discharging or abreacting experiences of high emotional intensity and significance through the normal channels of feeling, thought, and action. These poorly processed emotional experiences give rise to a persistent state of dammed-up inner tension; under further adverse conditions this may lead to abnormal and abortive types of discharge appearing in the form of hysterical symptoms. Through hypnotic therapy these now unconscious experiences re-emerge and the possibility of adequate discharge (abreaction) is provided in hypnosis, as in the case of Anna O., and with it the source of the symptom can be removed. This theory differs in two basic respects from Charcot's and Janet's, and both points are essential for the further development of psychoanalysis. The first difference lies in Freud's consideration that neurosis might befall relatively normal—not just congenitally degenerated—personalities under special critical circumstances which, at that time, he and Breuer ascribed to states of exhaustion. Secondly, the theory introduces into psychology a dynamic concept—active emotional forces leading to intrapsychic tension and pressure.

Freud gave up hypnosis in the treatment of his patients

as a method too vigorous and too fallible at the same time. In place of this artificial condition he introduced what he called *free association*, a broader, more promising way of reaching forgotten memories, fantasies, and feelings.[1] He requested of his patients when searching for the meaning of a symptom during their session to make every effort not to suppress or brush aside anything and to try to give up logical control of their thoughts or any special plan to direct their conversation. Instead of this he asked them to try to express their thoughts, feelings, and images as they came into their minds. Ideas appeared then which had little to do with the patient's everyday life and behavior, and sometimes were even strange and alien to him. But they often proved to have a similar significance and effect as the thoughts originally retrieved in hypnosis. Freud also observed that the nearer a patient came to the pertinent experience or memory, to the "clue" of the symptom, the more difficult was it for him to talk and the more painful or embarrassing became the content of his thoughts, so that he had to use a great deal of self-discipline not to omit the material again and not to veer off into other topics.

Slowly, Freud gained the conviction that these unconscious ideas had not disappeared from the patient's awareness by chance, by a state of exhaustion, but that the patient must have once tried to get rid of them because of their unpleasant nature by pushing them out of his conscious mind, i.e., by "repressing" them as Freud named it. The reasons for this repression were the same ones which made the patient want to avoid recalling them in treatment: either because they were frightening or embarrassing or difficult to tolerate. The thoughts and feelings thus repressed were forced out of the patient's awareness, but remained unresolved within his unconscious mind, retaining their emotional charge. Because of this charge they continually try to emerge from their psychic exile and have to be persistently held in abeyance. On certain

---

[1] The introduction of "free association" illustrates how an improved method of observation advances scientific research.

critical occasions they break through in the disguised form of the neurotic symptom. Among the events which disturb or weaken the achieved equilibrium between the repressing forces and the repressed impulses are severe disappointments, losses, frustrations, or traumata in later life.

In order to elucidate this process, which seemed to play a basic part not only in hysteria but also in other forms of neurosis, Freud used the analogy of hydrodynamics: if we obstruct a powerful spring, the water will try to find an outlet and in all probability, after some time and by many detours, it will break through in an entirely different place or it will turn the region into a swamp. Similarly, the repressed unconscious impulse may break through later on without disclosing its original source and its true nature. Thus the sudden paralysis of Breuer's patient did not spontaneously reveal the memory of the original painful scene which she had tried to forget. If in hypnosis or in psychoanalysis we penetrate the disguise of the symptom and the repressed recollection becomes conscious again, an opportunity is provided for the discharge of affects and there is no further necessity for the neurotic substitute outlet.

In order to avoid a misconception it might be important to note that Freud never held that everything forgotten was repressed. There is a less fateful way of forgetting unacceptable impulses than by repressing them. As children or adults, when the need arises we can use the technique of *suppression* against a variety of inner experiences, from an outburst of anger when we find it most unbefitting, to certain wishes and longings which we know cannot be fulfilled at this moment, to anxious reactions so that they do not interfere with our functioning. The difference between suppression and repression as they are used in psychoanalysis lies in the fact that the suppressed elements which have been removed from the center of our attention can be retrieved without too much difficulty if we put our minds to it seriously, whereas we speak of repression when this material cannot be brought back again simply by the power of our will. The psychological state in which these suppressed elements are comprised we call *preconscious*, in contrast to the *unconscious* of the deeply repressed.

From 1895 on, Freud conducted a continuously progressing investigation of these and similar phenomena until psychoanalysis represented an extensive and complex theoretical system. His method characteristically was concerned with collecting and grouping clinical observations, arriving at hypotheses, and testing them against new clinical data.[2] At the same time he modified and improved his therapeutic technique. For example, Freud (1905b) discovered that one of

[2] The following letter addressed to Dr. H. Löwy, in which Freud describes the method he applied in his scientific inquiry, was originally in the collection of Dr. Richard von Mises, Gordon McKay Professor of Aerodynamics and Applied Mathematics, Harvard University. It was given to Dr. Grete L. Bibring by his widow, Dr. Hilde von Mises.

Joseph Popper-Lynkeus (1838-1931), referred to in the first sentence, was an Austrian writer whose idealistic and humanitarian sociological contributions were highly valued by his contemporaries and appreciated by Freud (1932).

Wien IX Berggasse 19
30/3/1930

PROF. DR. FREUD

Dear Dr. Löwy:

Your biography of Popper-Lynkeus which you enclosed pleased me so much in its sincerity and dignity that I would like to fulfill your request, to add my contribution to your collection of samples of problem solutions in science. But I met in this attempt with remarkable obstacles which are difficult to overcome, as if certain expectations brought in from other areas (of science) could not be applied to the material with which I deal. Perhaps this is due to the fact that the experiment, which serves the physicist and physiologist, has no place in our work methods.

If I review the single steps in the development of my work, I always find that the conceptions [*Auffassungen*] offered themselves directly as the precipitate of a great number of impressions as I was gathering my experience. Whenever I was fortunate enough to recognize later on that one of these concepts was erroneous, it had always been substituted—and I hope to the better—in the following way: that a new idea entered my mind (based on the same and on additional, new experiences) to which I then subjected this material again.

I am afraid all this will not be of much use for your collection?

Respectfully yours,
Freud

the most important elements in the patient's relationship to the physician stemmed from the inevitable tendency of the patient to transfer unconsciously onto the physician strong expectations and feelings that he had held toward important figures in his past life. These *transference* feelings could cover a broad range from early childhood aggressive and hostile attitudes to strong dependent and erotic attachments. It was only after these transferences had been detected and understood that the therapy could attain its full potential and be brought to a successful conclusion. Freud (1910) recognized that transference was not limited to psychoanalysis but arose spontaneously in all close human affiliations. However, it develops with special intensity and significance in a patient's relationship to his physician.

In his further work Freud observed and could confirm that the search for the important repressed recollections or conflicts, ideas or wishes, regularly led far back into the patient's childhood. And so he added to his theories the concept that neurosis is due to repressed childhood experiences, even though the actual illness may break out in later years. This then led Freud to a very important, and in those days quite courageous, formulation, which provoked intense antagonism among his contemporaries. His observations taught him that the repressed childhood memories were of a very special kind, of an aggressive or sexual nature. Thus his theory of neurosis was broadened again, leading to the following fomulation: early infantile, instinctual experiences and fantasies which seem repugnant or for some other reason intolerable for the child will be rejected from consciousness, i.e., repressed.

By this discovery Freud replaced the then prevailing idea of the innocence of the child, untouched by any strong impulses, by his famous theory of the infantile, instinctual sexual and aggressive strivings; he had left here for the first time the theory of the neurosis itself and had turned his interest to the often equally inexplicable manifestations of normal psychological development. In the midst of his work with neurotic patients he succeeded in gaining an understanding of the function and structure of dreams. As with the neurotic symptom, there existed the tendency to call the dream psychologically meaningless because it seemed incomprehensible. As with the neurotic symptom, Freud (1900) could show that the dream represented a significant expression of unconscious tendencies, though the dream is the result of a normal, not a pathological, breakthrough of repressed impulses. Since the activity of our conscious mind is reduced during sleep, the censorship over rejected impulses slackens and unconscious tendencies can emerge with greater strength. They are expressed in the peculiar way of dream pictures and symbols in accordance with the mode of intellectual functioning characteristic of sleep, and probably close to the primitive thought processes of early childhood and archaic societies. Freud demonstrated that these symbols, like symptoms, can be understood through the ideas or memories and feelings which the dreamer associates with them.

Further studies by Freud and his co-workers dealt not only with the instinctual life but also with the ego and superego, and with personality formation. Psychoanalysis did not remain restricted to psychiatry and psychotherapy, but found its application in practically all fields concerned with the understanding of man like the humanities, social sciences, law, and education, as well as medicine in general.

In this sketchy outline we have tried to indicate the salient features of the development of psychoanalytic theory. We shall now attempt to test this complicated system in several of the various ways in which we can examine the validity of scientific hypotheses. As was already noted, these constructs, originally devised to help understand neurosis, could be applied successfully to new data, for example, to the dream. When we work within the framework of this system and become more and more familiar with our field and our individual patients, we can often anticipate probable developments and can sometimes make specific predictions with assurance. We become skillful in perceiving the underlying unity in certain events.

The following case history may serve to illustrate the theoretical concept of the neurotic symptom as the result of repressed unconscious conflicts. Repression in this case is clearly the final step in the psychological process by which the child attempts to reject and overcome unacceptable wishes or tendencies. The clinical data are as follows: Bobby, a five-year-old boy, reacts with aggressive jealousy to his newborn brother. His parents scold him angrily. The boy then gives up his hostile attitude and instead is found standing at the baby's crib, repeating, "We all love him, isn't he nice." Not long after this, a delegation of mothers from the neighborhood arrives with the complaint that Bobby, who had been such a nice boy, lately has been torturing smaller playmates maliciously, destroying their toys, and throwing sand in their eyes. Bobby is punished by not being allowed to go to the playground. He has to stay home for a period, and after that the complaints cease. Then Bobby develops nightmares with the following content: something happens to his baby brother, Davy; Davy is kidnapped; there is a fire in which everyone escapes except the baby who is burned up; an automobile hits Davy and he is quite dead. At the same time Bobby develops anxieties: he wants the baby's crib placed in his own room so that he can be sure that no more bad dreams of something happening to the baby will come; Bobby, who by then goes to kindergarten, develops a new fear that something may go wrong at home, that his brother and parents will be in a disaster and he will not find them any more when he comes home. He refuses to leave his family in the morning, and shows the symptoms of a school phobia.

We assume as our explanatory construct that one and the same aggressive jealousy lies behind the three groups of phenomena: the initial jealousy of the baby brother; the attacks on other children in the park; and Bobby's fearful fantasies about the disaster which befalls Davy. The implication of the construct is that a hostile impulse directed against a certain object (baby brother) can be shifted or displaced to related objects (other children), providing some satisfaction of vengeance. Then the original jealousy can be transformed further by repressing the impulse, removing it from conscious awareness, so that no direct gratification is possible. Instead, anxiety over the derivatives of the repressed impulse appears as the symptom (represented in the disaster fantasies). Although the aggressive impulse can no longer be detected by direct observation, the theory which we proposed links the three groups of phenomena in a satisfactory way. The validity of the theoretical concept can be further established by psychoanalytic investigation of a number of cases where, behind similar symptoms, similar data can be remembered, reconstructed, and verified by the environment.

What about predictability? Neurotic disturbances are frequently predictable from family constellations, not in detail but in general. As a matter of fact, Bobby's case had been predicted in a discussion of sibling rivalry in which his parents were involved shortly before the baby brother was born. His parents denied the significance of this conflict and felt that the behavior problems of children after the arrival of a new baby are the unfortunate results of taking such matters too seriously. They intended to demonstrate that such a development in their older child could be prevented by "old-fashioned" discipline. Against their point of view the discussion emphasized that this approach might interfere with the normal resolution of the sibling rivalry conflict and favor pathological solutions through repression. When these parents later sought the help of a child psychiatrist for Bobby's phobia, it gradually became apparent to them that through their attitude they may have contributed to the outcome, which had been predicted in the discussion.

With regard to verification by planned experiment we

are definitely at a disadvantage compared with the natural sciences and with experimental psychology. It is, in spite of our ever-growing interest and effort, almost impossible to set up repeatable experiments which come close to life experience. How could we, within the limits of professional ethics, create artificially for the purpose of study a conflict so overwhelming that our subject will have to repress it? Nevertheless, some concepts have been tested by experiment, including one of the most disputed ones, that of dream symbols representing sexual dream thoughts. Investigators told patients in hypnosis sexual stories in which the patients played a part and ordered them to dream the stories the next night (Schroetter, 1911; Roffenstein, 1924; Nachmansohn, 1925). It was very interesting to find that the well-known and often ridiculed symbols appeared in place of the crude sexual content in the following dreams. Betlheim and Hartmann (1924) told frankly sexual stories to patients with Korsakoff psychosis. Persons with this disorder have a marked impairment of immediate recollection based upon organic disorder of the brain, and compensate by confabulation. When these patients attempted to repeat the stories, sexual symbols like climbing stairs or knifing the partner replaced the direct sexual details. Experiments testing other aspects of psychoanalytic theory followed, many on animals, but all of these, as you will well understand, were not as satisfactory as the other approaches which played an ever-increasing role in psychoanalytic research: to compare our constructs, which were gained on patients in later life, with direct observations on children; or to study life situations which work like experiments as in the case of Bobby, or, on a large scale, the impact of war and its effect on children (A. Freud and Burlingham, 1942, 1943; Bonnard, Frankl, and Robinson, 1949).

Dr. Lester F. Beck (1952) produced a film, *Unconscious Motivation*, which may serve us as an illustration of a planned experiment. In the film two college students, a boy and a girl, were hypnotized together. Under hypnosis he gave them essentially the following instructions: "You are six years old. On your way home from school you find a red purse containing two shiny coins which belongs to one of your friends. Although you know it is the wrong thing to do, you buy chewing gum with the money and throw away the purse. Your mother asks you how you got the gum and you lie and feel very badly about it. Your conscience continues to bother you and shows itself in devious ways in your present adult life. I shall awaken you now, and in a few moments when I rap on the table, each of you will have a dream about this incident."

When he awakened them at this point, they did not remember what the hypnotist had told them, yet without knowing why, each of them felt tense and uncomfortable. The girl looked clearly upset and depressed and the boy complained about perspiration and restlessness. When the hypnotist rapped on the table, the girl drifted off into a daydream while the boy fell asleep briefly. When questioned about this, both said that some thoughts had occurred to them.

The girl reported that she saw herself at a carnival and there was a spinning red disc; she was on it and could not get off. She wanted to get off, but there were two chunky men with long arms standing at the edge holding hands, and they did not permit her to leave. She was quite anxious, but it was as if she were glued to the disc; and now, though fully awake, she still felt upset and worried as if she had done something wrong.

The boy said that he had dreamed of going somewhere, like to a fair, but he had first to go through a forest. There must have been a storm because the trees were whipping down on him. They were closing in so he ran. There were round pebbles on the ground and he felt compelled to pick them up though he was in such a hurry. He felt ashamed. It seemed silly to be trying to run away from something and yet stopping to pick up pebbles. Then he was at the fair and everything seemed nice, but it seemed wrong for him to be there.

During the remainder of the film the hypnotist attempted to help the two students associate to their dreams through ink blots, pictures, and a series of words, and to let them gradually bring out all of the "forgotten" elements so that they could remember the whole underlying story of their theft. The film demonstrated impressively how with this reconstruction the depression and anxiety vanished, and interest and the pleasure of disentanglement replaced the former mood. This experiment not only illustrates to a certain degree the representation of an unconscious conflict in the language of the dream, but also the resolution of such a disturbing conflict through recovery of memories and feelings pertaining to the "repressed." It further provides the opportunity to observe the different ways in which individuals express and attempt to cope with their unconscious feelings of guilt.

SUGGESTED READING

It may be desirable throughout these lectures to consult texts and reference works dealing with essential components of medical psychology and psychiatry, with their historical background and scientific methods. In addition to the following basic works, specific reading, related to topics as they emerge, will be suggested at the end of each main Part of this book, and in Appendix I can be found a supplementary list of reference works.

Basic Reading

Engel, G. L. (1962), *Psychological Development in Health and Disease* (Philadelphia: Saunders). A textbook for medical students which presents systematically the biological, psychological, and social factors in human development, and the correlations between physiological and psychological development.

Erikson, E. H. (1950), *Childhood and Society* (New York: Norton). Examines the interaction of individual development with the social environment.

Freud's classical general introduction to psychoanalysis is to be found in: Introductory Lectures on Psycho-Analysis (1916-1917) (*Standard Edition*, Vols. 15 & 16), and New Introductory Lectures on Psycho-Analysis (1933) (*Standard Edition*, 22:3-182). The editors of *The Standard Edition* have supplied references that make these lectures an introduction to Freud's writings as well as to psychoanalysis in general. Since the lectures are interconnected, it might be best to read them through at least once. In the opening lecture, and repeatedly throughout the series, Freud discusses the difficulties that people encounter in approaching the observations and generalizations of psychoanalysis. The early lectures are concerned with such phenomena as slips of speech and dreams, which are explained by the theory of unconscious mental processes. Lectures V to XV are a compendium of

Freud's discoveries about the dream. Neuroses, especially hysteria and obsessional neurosis, are discussed from Lecture XVI onward, particularly in Lectures XVII, XVIII, and XXI to XXIV. The meaning of symptoms and their relationship to childhood experiences, sexual development and frustration in adult life occupy Lectures XVII to XXIV. Note the concept of a complemental series in the etiology of neurosis (Lecture XXII). Contributions of psychoanalysis to the theoretical understanding of the psychoses (paranoia, depression, schizophrenia) are mentioned in various places (e.g., Lectures XVI, XXIV, and XXVI), centering in a discussion of narcissism (Lecture XXVI). Lectures XX and XXI present Freud's view of sexuality and its development in the individual. His initial concept of anxiety, its origins and place in mental life, is stated in Lecture XXV. Further experience, which resulted in the formulation of the ego, superego, and id constituting the structure of personality (Lecture XXXI), also led him to revise fundamentally the theory of anxiety (Lecture XXXII). For Freud's discussion of psychoanalysis as a therapy, see especially Lecture XIX on resistance and repression, Lecture XXVII on the transference, and Lecture XXVIII on hypnotism, suggestion, and the transference. Lecture XXXIII is devoted to the development and psychology of women.

Zilboorg, G. & Henry, C. W. (1941), *A History of Medical Psychology* (New York: Norton).

Adaptation, Adjustment and Personality

Bibring, G. L., Dwyer, T. F., Huntington, D. S., & Valenstein, A. F. (1961), A Study of the Psychological Processes in Pregnancy and the Earliest Mother-Child Relationship. *The Psychoanalytic Study of the Child*, 16:9-72. See pp. 62-72 (Glossary of Defenses).

Freud, A. (1936), *The Ego and the Mechanisms of Defense* (New York: International Universities Press, rev. ed., 1966).

Freud, S. (1933), New Introductory Lectures on Psycho-Analysis (*Standard Edition*, 22:3-182). Lecture XXXI ("The Dissection of the Psychic Personality") on the ego, superego, and id is especially pertinent to adaptation, adjustment, and personality.

Hartmann, H. (1939), *Ego Psychology and the Problem of Adaptation* (New York: International Universities Press, 1958).

PSYCHOANALYTIC PSYCHOLOGY AS A SCIENCE

Erikson, E. H. (1958), The Nature of Clinical Evidence. In: *Evidence and Inference*, ed. Daniel Lerner (Glencoe, Ill.: Free Press, pp. 73-95). Clinical inference is illustrated with the material of a psychotherapeutic hour.

Freud, S. (1916-1917), Introductory Lectures on Psycho-Analysis (*Standard Edition*, Vols. 15 & 16), and New Introductory Lectures on Psycho-Analysis (*Standard Edition*, 22:3-182). Lectures XVII to XXIV on the meaning of symptoms, Lectures XXV and XXXII on anxiety, and Lectures V to XV on the dream.

Hartmann, H. (1958), Comments on the Scientific Aspects of Psychoanalysis. *The Psychoanalytic Study of the Child*, 13:127-146. For the advanced reader.

Kaplan, A. (1964), *The Conduct of Inquiry* (San Francisco: Chandler Publishing Co.). Assesses and clarifies the application of scientific principles to the behavioral sciences.

Kris, E. (1947), The Nature of Psychoanalytic Propositions and Their Validation. In: *Psychological Theory*, ed. M. H. Marx (New York: Macmillan, 1951, pp. 332-351).

Pötzl, O., Allers, R. & Teler, J. (1917, 1924), *Preconscious Stimulation in Dreams, Associations and Images* [*Psychological Issues*, Monogr. 7] (New York: International Universities Press, 1960). Classical studies linking sensory physiology, experimental psychology, and psychoanalysis. In his introduction, Charles Fisher discusses a variety of recent related experimental approaches.

Pumpian-Mindlin, E., ed. (1952), *Psychoanalysis As Science* (Stanford: Stanford University Press). Ernest R. Hilgard discusses "Experimental Approaches to Psychoanalysis." Lawrence S. Kubie considers "Problems and Techniques of Psychoanalytic Validation and Progress." Eugene Pumpian-Mindlin discusses "The Position of Psychoanalysis in Relation to the Biological and Social Sciences."

Stewart, W. A. (1967), *Psychoanalysis: The First Ten Years, 1888-1898* (New York: Macmillan), concentrates upon Freud's scientific thinking during these years and relates it to the later development of psychoanalysis. Parts of this book are advanced reading. It may be helpful to read first one of the general expositions of psychoanalysis (Brenner, 1955; Freud, 1916-1917, 1933; Hendrick, 1958; Waelder, 1960).

Part II

CHILDHOOD DEVELOPMENT, PERSONALITY TYPES, AND MEDICAL MANAGEMENT

3

Infancy: The Central Needs

In the preceding chapter we have stressed that psychological conditions are not static. They must always be judged as an intrinsic part of the whole personality and as a result of each person's entire history. We depicted, in a preliminary fashion, the developmental process whereby the child learns to control his instinctual impulses in order to adapt and adjust to the adult world; as this adaptive effort becomes organized and stabilized, the methods of adjustment used by the child result in various normal behavioral tendencies. Under special conditions they may lead to the development of a neurosis. In order to prepare the way for a more complete consideration of personality development we discussed the history and methodology of our approach to understanding human psychology. As we now describe the course of psychological development starting in earliest childhood, we shall take up at the same time the shaping of personality and certain aspects of the origin and management of psychopathological reactions. We shall focus upon the kinds of problems that physicians face rather than upon those that are the particular concern of the psychiatric specialist.

We have depicted the newborn infant as a predominantly instinctual being with uncoordinated, urgent drives,

43

without personal knowledge or experience of the outside world, without emotional attachments to the outside world, and without any psychological or physical control over himself, but with a potential for more differentiated and discriminating functioning.

The baby's leading needs center around food and comfort. His mouth is an area where intense experiences of stimulation occur in a constant rhythm of frustration and satisfaction. His first regular contact with the outside world is through being fed and cared for by his mother (or mother surrogate). Through these gratifying experiences he gains his initial and strongest attachment to another person. Mother's presence is associated with satisfaction and we infer that her absence is linked with hunger and frustration; very soon food and mother's love become amalgamated in the baby's mind.

We adults have various means and ways of living out and expressing our feelings: when we feel restless, we take a walk in the evening; when we are full of hopes and expectations, we may listen to music or drink a highball; when we are attracted by someone, we can write letters, read poetry or make love; when we are disappointed, we knock things about, shout at our friends or pick on our family; when we hate, we start a big intrigue or we attack the enemy squarely or do hundreds of other things depending upon our preferences and our abilities.

The baby is much more limited in what he can do. According to our understanding, after he has learned to know the satisfaction through feeding, he wants to repeat this pleasurable experience even independently of hunger and food. He wants to swallow or suck when he likes something and he wants to spit out or bite what he hates. That is why a baby of five to ten months or older often does not take food even though he is hungry if a new nurse, a strange, not loved person wants to feed him; but whether he is or is not hungry, he opens his mouth wide in pleasure and happiness when his mother bends over his crib. That is, food and love represent the same value for him; disappointment in food or love can create the same difficulties, and the first behavioral problems may start in this phase. We call this initial stage of development the *oral phase* because of the emotional and maturational importance of the mouth; the oral phase reaches its height in the early part of the first year and lasts for approximately a year or a little longer.

A social worker consulted me a while ago about a case that can further our understanding of the nature and problems of the oral phase. Mrs. B., a young, intelligent woman who had contacted the agency for financial help, complained about her six-month-old boy. Johnny was a child with an unclear and undiagnosed, but persistent gastrointestinal disturbance. He looked thin, pale, underdeveloped, unhappy, and sickly. After meals he showed signs of discomfort, or perhaps pain, and cried bitterly for hours. Careful examinations at the hospital had shown no evidence of physical disease. Mrs. B. felt desperate and helpless. She had done her best; she kept strictly to a book on hygiene for babies, did not omit anything advised in that book or permit herself any indulgence in the upbringing of the child. No meals had been given in between the correct times, even when her sleep was disturbed by the baby's crying during the first weeks. She had never spoiled or excited him unduly by carrying him around. For the same reason she refrained from taking him up at meals and did not feed him on her lap, but propped up in his crib. Nevertheless, the child did not gain, he fretted, ailed, and was obviously in poor condition.

This social worker did not really need my advice because she confessed that before she could ask my opinion, she had already expressed her own ideas to the mother, which were dictated not by book studies but by the healthy reaction of her warm personality. She had said that such a strict regime might be extreme even for a healthy baby, let alone for a child who seemed to suffer from pain and be unhappy. It certainly could not harm the baby to be taken up and played with by his mother. The report that the amazed mother gave to the equally surprised worker three weeks later showed an unexpected success, and by that revealed the cause of the child's mysterious illness: supported by the authority of the worker, Mrs. B. had permitted herself to be natural and to show the child the normal, unhygienic warmth of a mother, with the result that Johnny lost his alarming symptoms. He seemed happy, ate astonishingly well, gained weight, and did not show signs of pain or sickness.

In this connection we want to add some material from the case of a four-and-a-half-year-old boy called Paul that was related to us by a colleague who had observed him in an institution.[1] Paul had been sent by a hospital for special observation to clarify his diagnosis. It was not apparent whether he was severely mentally retarded or an extremely emotionally disturbed, pseudoimbecilic child. When the observer met him for the first time, Paul was lying in his bed. He did not look up when somebody came to the bed; he did not listen when people tried to attract his attention by calling his name or whistling or making noises next to him; he did not turn his head or even move his eyes. From time to time Paul got up in his bed and started to run back and forth with an anxious, tense expression on his face. When a toy was given to him, he immediately threw it far away. On other occasions he would repeatedly bang his head against the bed, pinch and lacerate his skin, and pull out his hair. He had never learned to speak. He ate little and constantly turned his head to the side when the nurse tried to feed him, so that in two and a

---

[1] It was Dr. O. Hobart Mowrer, Research Professor in the Department of Psychology, University of Illinois, who had studied Paul at the Children's Community Center, New Haven, Connecticut, and who has kindly consented to our use of this case.

half years he had only gained a pound and a half. He never smiled and never cried.

The observer took a great interest in the child. He even brought him into his own home, feeling that this might be a good thing for a child who had so little friendly contact with the world; and slowly Paul changed. He started to eat, to play, to cry, to smile, even to laugh, and to learn a few words. His restlessness and attacks of anxiety stopped and returned only once for a short period when Paul's foster parents, the observer and his wife, fell ill at the same time and had to go to a hospital, and Paul was cared for by other members of the institutional staff. He again stopped eating, did not permit anyone to touch him, threw things at people, and calmed down completely only after his friends returned from the hospital.

We can interrupt our story here and ask a question. What has happened to this child in the past that might perhaps explain his difficulties and his extraordinary behavior? Before he lived in his new home he was a human being completely without any visible contact with the outside world, without even having started the usual means of establishing contact like paying attention, trying to speak, smiling and playing; and more than that, without any intention of taking up this contact, and refusing even to accept food that was offered to him.

When we tell you Paul's prior history, his behavior will probably become more understandable. Paul was a foundling who had been discovered starving in an empty apartment when he was about ten days or two weeks old. He was taken to an orphanage, a well-run institution giving all the care necessary for a child's normal physical development, but probably, as far as we could judge, too rigid for a child who had had such a traumatic experience. It seems that nobody there ever could give him enough attention and love for his special needs and thus he never recovered from his earliest deprivation, until the day when, for the first time in his life, two warm and friendly people turned their hearts to him. This then pulled him out of his isolation and made it possible for him to try out his first moves toward other people.

Paul's very dramatic story is in a certain way significant for our problem because it shows how early lack of food can be aggravated by early lack of love and create a most pathological reaction in a child. If we place next to this case the one of Johnny B. related by the social worker, where lack of any expression of warmth to the child represented the pathogenic factor, and a third kind of case where in the early history a severe gastrointestinal disturbance existed, like cases of pylorospasm, then we can see the following: in all of these instances similar psychological difficulties occur, ranging from eating problems to disturbance of the child-mother relationship and the further object relationships of the child. However, there is a difference between these cases which at first approach may seem a little startling: the adverse effect of continued lack of human closeness proves to be more serious, more far-reaching than food deprivation per se ever can be.

The most extreme forms of such disturbances were observed among institutionalized children like Paul. In the past a high percentage of babies brought up in institutions died of the average infectious diseases of infancy, as if they lacked the drive to live. The surviving children frequently showed a retardation of physical, intellectual, and social development which resulted in asocial, intellectually deficient, psychotic or "problem" behavior (Bender and Yarnell, 1941; Bakwin, 1942, 1949; W. Goldfarb, 1945; Spitz, 1945, 1946; Spitz and Wolf, 1946; Beres and Obers, 1950; Bowlby, 1951; Provence and Ritvo, 1961; Provence and Lipton, 1962). These stark clinical findings were augmented in experimental studies like those of Harry F. Harlow (1958, 1961, 1962) and his associates who raised rhesus macaque monkeys under various conditions of separation from their mothers and isolation from other monkeys.

A number of investigators had noted that newborn monkeys raised apart from their mothers became strongly attached to gauze diaper pads used to carpet the floors of their cages. This was reminiscent of the way human infants are devoted to favorite blankets or soft toys (Winnicott, 1953). Harlow's group discovered further the grim fact that if the cloth pads were removed, hardly any of the rhesus babies survived the first five days of life on the bare wire-mesh cage floor. But these newborns throve if a cone made of wire-mesh and preferably covered with terry cloth was introduced into the cage. They hugged the cone much as they normally would cling to their mothers, spending eighteen hours daily this way. While these conditions of contact with the artificial wire and cloth "surrogate mother," plus bottle feeding in the security of a cage, seemed to provide nurturance and protection, many other elements necessary for normal maturation were lacking. A live monkey mother not only safeguards her infant until it can respond to danger signals, but helps it become socially responsive. She enables or forces it gradually to relax its dependence, and to explore the environment and play with other monkey infants. When opportunity for interaction with the mother is delayed or limited, the rhesus baby remains tied to the mother and incapable of affection toward other infants.

In the most extreme form of this experimental maternal deprivation, baby monkeys separated from their mothers at birth and not permitted direct physical contact with other infants appeared less and less normal as they grew to maturity. They sat mutely staring into space, indifferent to stimuli, clutched their heads and rocked or went into violent rages. Upon reaching the age of physical maturity their sexual responses, even with normal partners, were totally inadequate or inappropriate. When it was possible, with great effort, to have a few of these females impregnated, they failed miserably as mothers, appearing utterly helpless, abusive of their offspring, or devoid of maternal feeling. The early presence of a cloth "surrogate mother" seemed to mitigate the severity of this personality damage; and given the opportunity in infancy to form patterns of affectionate behavior with other infants rather than being raised in complete physical isolation, the monkeys could develop normal sexual responses.

To return now to our human infants and to more common and less severe forms of maternal deprivation: for instance, if the mother due to her own inner difficulties or to external conditions cannot devote herself fully to her baby, or even if the child feels threatened in this relationship by the arrival of a sibling, then we still see the effect of a less intense deprivation in those unhappy, crying children, always under the inner tension of a need, always "hungry," always dissatisfied, greedy, and jealous, full of resentment as if something essential was withheld from them, and often showing eating difficulties as one expression of this disappointment.

It is frequently observed that children whose eating problems are largely based upon early conflict with their mothers very often can eat well when the mother is absent. Several years ago a young woman, Mrs. C., came to our clinic quite upset and discouraged. Her little girl of three offered a terrible problem to her because she could not make the child eat. Alison was one of those children who keeps the first bite hidden in her cheek for the rest of the day. The child was very thin, obviously somewhat underdeveloped, but healthy looking and very charming. Mrs. C. herself had an interesting history. As a young girl she suffered from a phobia of tuberculosis. Her family doctor told her to get married and then everything would be alright. She took his advice and, oddly enough, she then lost her phobia. It would distract us if we discussed at this point the wisdom of such medical advice. What is of interest to us is that when she had her first child, the little girl about whom she was now so concerned, she developed the very same anxiety about tuberculosis, but now it was not related to herself but to this baby. It took the form of a fear that Alison might not eat enough and thus become susceptible to the disease. The mother's neurotic preoccupation with food created a special tension around eating and this tension had its ill effects on the child.

Mrs. C. was advised by us not to force her daughter but rather, when the little girl kept food in her mouth for a while, to quietly disregard it and thus allow her to slowly discover on her own that she was hungry. However, the mother could not carry this through; when she removed a plate with uneaten food, though she did not say anything, she would "grind her teeth in despair," and it was apparent that the little girl was aware of this reaction in her mother. One day, somewhat later, Mrs. C. reported with a mixture of amusement and embarrassment that she had placed the child in a day care center and had prepared the staff carefully for what they would have to go through with her child at meals. When she came to call for her daughter on the first day, everybody smiled at her and told her that Alison had eaten heartily just like any other youngster in the group. Clearly, here the symptom was based on a problem between the child and the mother, and represented a willful reaction of the child to pressures stemming from the preoccupation of her mother.

You will readily understand that a disturbance in the mother-child relationship does not necessarily imply a conscious rejection on the part of the parent. A variety of factors may be involved in the actual life situation. For example, the mother may have emotional problems which interfere with her relating herself positively to the child; these may be of a transitory nature, for example, when the mother gets upset over distressing events in the family, or they may represent a neurosis or personality disorder. The mother may be unable to care for the young child because of physical illness or the child may have to be hospitalized or, for some other reason, separated from the mother at an early age. The mother's attention may have been withdrawn out of necessity when a new baby came into the family.

In contrast to the behavior of Alison who refused food so persistently, we saw Betty, an eight-year-old child who was grossly overweight and, as her mother said, always ate two or three helpings. Yet here too the symptom stemmed from difficulties in her early life situation. Her mother, Mrs. D., informed us that Betty had been very nice and easy to care for up to the age of four when the mother became pregnant. Something unexpected and apparently traumatic occurred at that time. The mother's lying-in period was prolonged for about three weeks by an intercurrent infection. Betty, who had not been prepared for her mother's long absence, became afraid of the dark, cried, and refused to go to bed. After Mrs. D. had returned home for only a short while, she developed phlebitis and had to be rehospitalized for several weeks. From then on Betty was a difficult child and a number of special problems developed. First of all, she had a bad relationship with the baby, but what became more impressive was her intense greediness about food. She started to overeat and at the same time she showed the conflict over feeling displaced in her mother's affection by complaining bitterly whenever she found somebody sitting in her chair at the table; she would not sit down in the chair any more for that meal. The same possessiveness showed itself in her refusal to eat a piece of bread if somebody else had touched it before.

Soon afterward the little girl started to pack a little suitcase which she had received for Christmas and went around to people's apartments asking if she might move in, saying that she liked them and she would want to be their child. It was a game which Mrs. D. did not appreciate but tolerated because it was not terribly disturbing to the older couples in the building and everybody seemed to have a good time. The interest in this game passed after a while, but something else much more alarming took place.

Betty started to come home from school rather late. For quite some time the mother accepted the little girl's explanation that she had been playing with her friends until one day she received a call from the Society for the Prevention of Cruelty to Children. Her child had been picked up in a home nearby where she had been begging for a piece of bread or something else to eat, saying that she had no money and that nobody was at home where she lived to feed her. It turned out that Betty visited a number of homes in that way every day after school. She made her appeal so nicely that people usually gave her something to eat. Finally, the S.P.C.C. was called in because she had started to tell a different story. She said that her mother had gone on a trip leaving her alone in the house and had not provided for her. The people who heard this tale became alarmed and this is how the agency was called in.

This history reveals dramatically the whole problem of a child who feels deprived and unwanted, and who acts out her need for more care and love (food), turning to strangers for what she believes she cannot receive from her mother.

When a child's needs in the earliest period of life are too strong to be satisfied sufficiently by normal means, or when his normal needs are not satisfied because of a lack of response from his environment, the experience may serve as a trauma which he sometimes cannot overcome completely. We call the persistence of these unfulfilled needs a *fixation* in development, in the case of these children, an oral fixation. As the child grows up, the form in which such an unconscious conflict is expressed usually changes. The conflict may be transferred from mother to other women or to people who play an important part in the person's life similar to that of mother. It may be lived out in specific personality formations or expressed in symptoms. In the case of Paul, as we have seen, his initial eating symptom did not disappear but spread and found the strongest expression in a more metaphorical way: refusing to accept anything that people offered him, combined with complete withdrawal from the bad world. In other instances, the original oral impulse may persist directly as a ravenous appetite or prolonged thumb sucking, which can continue compulsively for many years; or, finally, in adulthood it may lead to drug addiction or alcoholism (as it did in the case of Mr. A., the man who craved alcohol in reaction to the birth of his son, just as he had earlier wanted cocoa when his little brother displaced him).

We sometimes find that children with early oral symptoms will have trouble in learning later on; they may neither refuse nor excessively demand food, but instead the problem will have shifted to a difficulty in taking in knowledge. Great frustration during the oral period may lead to rage or to depression and the kind of withdrawal, apathy, or lack of will to live that we saw in Paul's case. Later on in life the more serious depressive states often occur when the defenses of a person with intense oral fixations break down. In general, early traumatization can disrupt maturation and integration of personality functioning. It can act as an important predisposing factor in the development of serious emotional disturbances or even psychotic states, which abound in impulses and reactive modes typical of the oral period. Similarly, some psychosomatic illnesses can arise in the combination of a physiological condition and an oral fixation.

These serious disturbances are not the only or even the most common outcome of such fixations. Much more frequently, within the framework of normal development, they result in certain characteristic personality formations. In clinical practice we often encounter patients whom we may describe as "oral personalities." The more marked forms in this category usually present certain difficulties to physicians. These are the patients with the persistent, open or hidden claims upon the physician: they demand your special attention, need and expect your care in everything, ask for your advice and help in the simplest problems of their lives which they are certainly capable of deciding themselves, and follow you around as if trying to swallow you up completely. You will have the greatest trouble, on the one hand, to protect yourself against this assault and, on the other hand, not to become so anxious that you react aggressively and find yourself incapable of working with them. Such a patient almost invariably irritates and alarms his "victims" to such an extent that they try to protect themselves as if they unconsciously recognized the patient's irresistible and insatiable craving.

If the patient's early experiences were not too frustrating and provided some feeling of satisfaction, he may put himself into the hands of the doctor in a naïve, childlike way, optimistically expecting all of the doctor's attention and care. Since his anticipation of unlimited attention and interest is experienced in a less imperative way, we generally find the situation tolerable and more easily manageable. When disappointment predominated in the oral phase, the personality reaction in later life may take on the aspect of a pessimistic expectation and a repetition of disappointment, rage, and depression or apathy. He may be hypersensitive to any sign of lack of consideration in others. This may even reach the proportions of a paranoid trend. The frequency with which these infantile remnants are observed in medical practice is due to the following fact: a person who in his normal life situation can still cope adequately with unresolved unconscious conflicts regresses under the impact of illness to more childlike reactions, especially when he must remain in bed passively under the care of nurses.

At this point let us consider the medical management of the oral personality, disregarding the more severe psychopathological conditions which become the special concern of the psychiatrist. We shall start with these problems and their management in the care of sick children and we shall discover that similar principles apply to the care of adult patients.

For some time there existed the notion that you can see at work in Paul's case and in the books on hygiene for babies which so many young mothers studied so carefully. It stated that young infants need only their peace, cleanliness, and regular routine in feeding and sleeping. These are important points, but certainly are not everything a baby needs.

Years ago there appeared in a professional journal a very interesting report on a model children's home with excellent hygienic conditions and routine of care. This home employed a cleaning woman, a friendly, fat, old lady who went through the wards daily to do the rough work. She was in the habit of stopping at the babies' beds, here and there, talking to them, and it seemed obvious to the doctors that both partners enjoyed it immensely.

The doctors soon discovered that the children who were brought up in this "ideal" environment never looked as happy and beaming as when old Marie stopped at their cribs to smile at them with her very simple, unsophisticated, but warm smile. So they tried to take advantage of Marie and whenever they had an infant or a young child who did not respond well to their routine, either did not gain weight, or did not seem to thrive without a clear medical reason, they handed him over, so to speak, to Marie. She then took the baby with her on her rounds, though we may find it difficult to imagine that in that sterilized atmosphere a baby was being carried around by the cleaning woman, just as he would have been carried around by his mother, grandmother, or aunt in a simple household, where nobody could stop working to take care of a child. Marie took him along, put him down in a chair while scrubbing this part of the floor, then on a table when cleaning another part, taking him up for a while, and talking baby talk to him. You may already have guessed the enormous therapeutic success of old Marie. These children soon lost their institutional symptoms and caught up with the more vigorous babies.[2]

----

[2] It was a pleasant surprise to discover this very same episode many years later (with "old Marie" presented as "old Anna") reported by an eyewitness, Dr. Fritz B. Talbot (1941).

What we learned from this experience of Marie and the doctors in the children's home has an important implication for everyday hospital practice. Anna Freud (1952) wrote about the emotional and mental effects of bodily illness in children, and her observation were supported and confirmed by many others. She noted that parents, when describing the neurotic disorders of their children, frequently date back the onset of the trouble to some bodily illness after which the child appeared to be "different." Mood swings, changes in the relationship to parents and siblings, loss of self-confidence, temper tantrums, often appear for the first time during convalescence after a severe illness. Symptoms such as bed wetting, soiling, feeding and sleeping troubles, and school phobias, which had existed and been overcome earlier in life, may reappear. Changes in intellectual performance may occur.

Among the potentially upsetting influences at the time of illness are hospitalization, the giving up of independent bodily functions (washing, dressing, initiative in bowel evacuation, etc.) occasioned by nursing procedures, restriction of movement, operations, and pain. Hospitalization in very young children can be regarded as a prototype of short-term separation from home and is attended by the misery and anxiety which also arise when young children are removed from their parents, placed in unfamiliar surroundings, and handled and cared for by strangers (Bowlby, Robertson, and Rosenbluth, 1952).

Without taking up the many interesting problems involved in what operations and pain signify to children of various ages and levels of psychological development (see Bergmann and A. Freud, 1965), we single out the factor of separation from home during this oral, early period as especially important. If it is at all possible, the child's separation anxiety should be minimized by having the mother accompany and remain with him during hospitalization. If this is not feasible, the mother should see the child as often and for as long as can be arranged even when the routine of the ward must be altered to accommodate such visiting. This is strongly advised because of its importance for both the child and the mother. The nurse or other person who replaces the mother in taking care of the physical needs of the child should be a warm, friendly, unsentimental, motherly type; for the essential needs of this age this is much more important than high intellectual ability. Frequent changes of personnel and the dropping in and out of volunteer helpers should be avoided in order to provide a stable, secure environment. Hospitalization need not represent only a potentially damaging experience, but under special circumstances the temporary removal of the child from a disturbing family situation might be of help (as in the day care center placement of Alison, pp. 50-51). Furthermore, in a hospital setting with experienced and knowledgeable personnel mother and child may have the opportunity to work out some conflicts and tensions which, without this intervention, would persist and lead to serious developmental difficulties (see Solnit, 1960).

It is important to note that even adult patients have a tendency to regress in their behavior to early childhood attitudes during acute illnesses, particularly if these conditions are exhausting, painful, disabling, life-threatening, or marked by mental confusion based upon toxic states. At such times the considerations that we have mentioned in the management of the hospitalization of very small children will often be applicable. The regular presence of a nurse familiar to the patient, or a close family member if this is practical, will encourage the patient to feel secure and protected, whereas being left entirely alone or exposed to numerous, changing staff and hospital personnel would add to his tension. The very anxious or delirious patient may be greatly reassured if someone whom he knows takes care of him at night and a small night light is left on. It is usually best if the person caring for the patient has a simple, friendly, undemanding approach. The emphasis in care is placed upon quietly meeting the patient's needs, even anticipating those he has not yet ex-

pressed. As much as this form of perceptive medical management is essential in the acute phase of his illness, we have to
remain flexible and modify our approach as the patient re-
covers. The return of his mature needs will have to be met by
our support of his reawakened interests and his desire for
greater independence.

However, there are adult patients in whom dependent
demands persist beyond childhood and reflect their special
personality structures, independent of the severity of their
illnesses. They pose an interesting problem for their medical
environment. To what extent should the doctors try to fulfill
such patients' demands? At what point might this make it
more difficult for the patient to recover because this gratification may offer too great a temptation for him to remain a
demanding child and he might abandon efforts to reach a level
of more mature functioning? An experience with a patient
some years ago may highlight this question.

In every medical setting, in hospitals and outpatient
clinics, we are used to finding a certain type of patient whose
main emotional needs seem to lead him back to the hospital,
to the doctor, and to the examination and medication which
he previously received. These are patients, for instance, who
are known to visit a number of clinics in the same morning,
to return to the hospital with all kinds of ill-defined complaints, and it is easy to perceive that these patients gain
something valuable from the available consideration and attention. They are usually recognizable by the size of their medical record files; they know the whole staff; they know the
employees; and they settle down, after a fashion, and make
the hospital their home. I suppose that every hospital has such
a veteran or mascot who appeared when the hospital door
opened for the first time and continued to return through all
the years. This type of patient very often belongs to the
personality type which has been described above, the childlike
person for whom the receiving of attention and small favors
is an important goal in life and who, for the sake of maintain-

ing this kind of simple and primitive gratification, will so often sacrifice much more important, realistic achievements.

One of these patients, Miss M., was an elderly woman who had been sent to the psychiatric clinic many years ago, not because of a circumscribed neurotic symptom but because there was the justified suspicion that part of her varied and manifold complaints were of an emotional nature. Furthermore, it was felt that the management of the patient required psychiatric intervention because she, like many others of this type, was not just demanding and in need of special attention; she was also inclined to react to frustration in a childlike way by temper tantrums, outbursts, complaints, and by immaturely attacking and running after people, so that the other services felt that psychiatric help and support for the patient might be of value for the professional staff as well.

I believe that the main reason for the referral of this patient to psychiatry stemmed from the kind of problems which in general arise between these oral dependent patients and their doctors. It seems that in the face of these persistent, excessive demands, doctors feel threatened and almost trapped. When this situation reaches a certain point, physicians tend to find some explanation, some rationalization for referring the patient and at least sharing the burden with another, unsuspecting colleague. I think that this may have been the main function of the psychiatric department for Miss M. The personality structure and the infantile needs of this patient were easily recognizable. One of the senior doctors took on the case and made a successful effort to establish a personal relationship which gave the patient a great deal of gratification and stabilized her needs. Whenever she believed that she was badly treated or neglected in one of the other clinics, instead of making a scene, she turned to the psychiatric department to have a talk with her favorite doctor. When he unfortunately had to leave the hospital, I inherited the patient from him. In my effort to manage the situation well I made a specific mistake which bears upon the question that I raised at the beginning of this case history.

I tried to help the patient accept the change of therapists and establish with me a similarly satisfactory contract. I probably went too far in my effort and overstepped the limits of necessary professional support. This happened one day when the patient overheard the enthusiastic remarks of other patients while standing in line for the cashier: two mothers discussed how the social service department had arranged for their children to go to summer camp; other women entered the conversation, one reporting that she had received a new orthopedic girdle and another mentioning that she had received new eyeglasses.

Miss M. came storming down to my office complaining about the fact that she was the only one who had not received these benefits. When I asked her whether she wanted to have a child sent to camp (she had no children), whether she needed a girdle, or if she wanted glasses, she had to admit that none of these things would be of any value to her. But, she proceeded to say, if she required something, she would not get it either. At this point, I challenged the statement and the patient, taking advantage of my weak position, said that she urgently needed a dress: "For months and months I have wanted to buy a dress; of course, you wouldn't do anything for me like that."

And there, losing my perspective and trying to prove something to the patient, I promised to give her the money for the dress. I did give her money; I won't tell you about the complication which such an action can create in a hospital setting with its well-organized channels of responsibility. In any case, it became quite clear to me that from this point on I could make no progress with the patient. It was as if I had opened a floodgate and what came through were her incessant demands, one more urgent than the other, and nothing else counted.

This proves to us that one cannot reach and truly fulfill unconscious infantile needs by concrete gifts. In spite of receiving the dress the very same doubts about whether she was as much loved as others forced her constantly to seek new proofs. As I did not want to go along with the impossible task of trying to give her all she demanded, I turned, for her, into a more rejecting person than all the figures around who had consistently resisted her pressures. I do not want to say that I could have truly helped this patient overcome her well-established, lifelong pattern, but I am certain that I could have handled it more successfully by continuing to reason with her and comfort her, temporizing and taking the edge off her demands to the point where she could make better use of the help the hospital offered. As it turned out, I had to transfer the patient to another therapist and for a considerable time the treatment went better, though a deteriorating process finally set in and led to increasing mental complications.

In the management of the oral personality two elements must be balanced, the fulfillment of urgent infantile needs and the setting of limits, bringing the patient to a point where he can accept restrictions. To be given to is the central desire, but, as in the case of Miss M., it may lead to problems. The first step in management is to establish in the patient the feeling that one will give what he truly needs, but that the line is drawn where his demands become compulsory, self-perpetuating, or excessive, or where they interfere with other important aspects of his care. Whatever you wish to achieve with such a person, you must first approach him with a positive acknowledgment of his need. For example, it has been found that in cases where one must prescribe a diet, the patient's feeling of frustration may be minimized if he knows that the doctor or dietician has paid particular attention, as far as it is permissible, to including his favorite dishes, and achieving the necessary restrictions by prohibiting the harmful food intake in those areas where he has less special preferences. Thus, a diabetic diet may be built up around an ice-cream soda. Where there is a diversified ethnic population it might be helpful to include traditional national dishes as part of the diet charts.

The way of setting limits in the face of the infantile requests of this type of patient may be illustrated in some everyday experience with children. What does a father do if he is busy writing letters and at the same time one of his children has had a distressing experience and wants to be comforted and have all of father's attention? From the child's point of view the problem is not that Daddy is writing important letters; for the child this means only: "He doesn't love me." The child demands the security of being loved, while the father wants him to grow up, to be able to recognize the importance of other realistic claims, and to permit the father to finish his work. The father may resolve this by striking a bargain with the child, first giving him the assurance that he is really loved and appreciated, and then requesting that the child give something to him in return. The father might say, "Would you let Daddy write the letter? It isn't that I don't like to play with you, but if the letter is not finished now, someone will be angry with me and scold me tomorrow. We will play later on."

In medical practice, setting limits is done by the doctor showing his willingness to satisfy the patient and by giving the patient a clear understanding that limits are set not because the doctor is impatient or lacking in concern but because of pressures to which even a doctor must submit. This is the form that is least painful for the patient, that provides him with an acceptable way of looking at the situation. For the demanding, oral person such a limit loses the meaning of a personal rejection and of not being loved, and it introduces the reality principle by which not only the patient but also his doctor must abide. This approach does not expect to achieve far-reaching changes in a patient, but nevertheless it introduces into the relationship something which has been missing in the patient since childhood, namely, the awareness that there are people who are devoted to his care and at the same time recognize limits and exercise control. Under these conditions the patient will not lose his dependent cravings, but his demands will become less pressing. And if the physician is prepared to stand by the patient, the latter will gain the necessary comfort and assurance of care by maintaining this contact and seeing his doctor a few times a year.

LECTURE

4

Early Mastery of Body Functions

As the child begins to emerge from the period of infancy, gaining muscular strength and coordination, pursuing his own goals and independent locomotion, starting to understand language and to speak, and asserting mastery over his own little world, he soon faces tasks and restricting demands directed against his unbridled ventures and enterprises, regulating his aggressive and willful expansiveness, and even requiring adjustment of his bodily functions beyond those associated with hunger and feeding. One of the central issues is that of toilet training, a prime example of the adaptive achievements which are expected from the young child in this period. Years ago the prevailing practice in child rearing demanded an early, rigid, strict program. Freud related a number of personality traits and difficulties to the struggle provoked by this traditional regime. People started to observe the problems which it created, the unhappiness of certain children or the behavior disturbances which seemed to begin at that time, and the frequent lack of success or relapses in the training of children who otherwise were quite well adjusted. The problems created by it for children as well as their mothers are frequently brought as presenting complaints to pediatric clinics.

65

Let us try to understand why a conflict develops at all: there is an urge for intense activity in the child of this age. The toddler never seems to stand still and hardly accepts any restriction of his movements. He reacts as if it were an imposition to be set down for his meal or to be put to bed before he is fully exhausted. In fact, he tends to resist almost any request or demand to regulate his activities. Moreover, from the start the child's attitude toward his excretory functions is very different from that of his adult environment. The young child is by no means disgusted about them, nor does he have a tendency to get rid of his body products as regularly and as quickly as possible. On the contrary, he is interested in them and pays special attention to them. He wants to take them up, to play with them, to paint with them if nobody interferes, to hold them back as long as he pleases, and to deposit them when he cannot hold them back any longer. This is reinforced by the very interesting fact that the anal mucous membrane is one of the special areas of the body from which, if stimulated, a physical pleasure can be derived. The growing child tends to cling to any kind of experience that provides pleasure. During toilet training the child's rather good relationship to his urine and feces has to change. The child must go from complete lack of bowel control to complete control.

In contrast to feeding, where the parent can remain a controlling agent, the child is expected to regulate bowel functioning by himself. Especially in cultures where toilet training is done with great pressure, the child will learn to regard this function as bad, ugly, and dirty, one which is not liked by the environment. Usually, most children after some rebellion accept this vigorous demand of their environment, adopt the regulations and restrictions, and become clean almost overnight. But some children go through a long and intense struggle at this time, which may be transformed into negativistic stubbornness and anger directed against any pressure or regulation, leading to what are called *anal character traits*.

When toilet training is introduced very early as was done in many cultures, particularly in English-speaking countries where the training was often begun before the child was able to sit up, you may find that the baby has complete bowel control by eight months to one year of age. Such training is established on a reflex basis as one would train an animal, and at times of intense emotional problems it may prove to be unstable and unreliable, and soiling and bed wetting return. With the evacuation of children during the Second World War in England this reaction was frequently observed in the three- and four-year-olds who had been trained very early. It presented a major problem for foster homes. Training is best done at a time when it is possible to explain and reason with the child rather than forcing him without his understanding. This is usually accomplished during the latter part of the child's second year. When the relationship between the child and the mother is good and comfortable, without special strains like illness of the parent or the child, the birth of a sibling, etc., then the youngster acquires a readiness for and interest in regulation.

A familiar outcome of the child's acceptance of toilet training is a shifting of some of the original interest to substitute activities: the preference for playing with dirty, messy materials such as mud pies, sand, clay, and finger paints. Those parents who are very rigid about toilet training are often also greatly concerned about dirt and dislike it even in transformed guise, so that they might close this outlet too for the child. Furthermore, the children's earlier interest in resisting parental pressure and retaining their own body products may later be expressed in the possessive zeal with which they collect little useless bits of string, papers, orange peels, pieces of chalk, and the like as something valuable that belongs to them. They defend their collections against anyone's decree to dispose of them and, if necessary, hide them carefully. This collector spirit often disappears in the course of growing up, but in some people it becomes stronger and more important with the years, retaining its original characteristics. There are grown people who cling to a collection of the very same materials, rationalizing it with: "One never knows, perhaps these articles may come in handy one day." These are the individuals who cannot discard anything, and often the smaller and less important the item is, the stronger is their attachment to it. During a wartime scrap drive in England the man in charge complained that "those who have most of the stuff collected don't give anything." This desire to gather and not to let go of anything one possesses, may again take another direction in later life, a trend toward the collecting of truly valuable objects, but even then there is usually much unrealistic urgency and oversensitivity about losses of any kind.

We should like to discuss this further, using as an example the widespread passion for collecting money which looks rather innocent indeed, but deserves our interest because of certain emotional elements. We do not refer to people who were poor and destitute and later develop an anxious grabbing, but to the miser who derives pleasure from the sheer hoarding of money. For the miser money has significance beyond its rational meaning; he does not regard it as something to be used and enjoyed as a means of attaining pleasure, and not even as a protection against future want and misery. It has become an important possession in itself, something which is highly charged emotionally and whose value is based upon trends of which the person is unaware. It might seem absurd to connect the miser with the child who cannot or does not wish to give up his stool. Yet, almost universally people refer to the habit of collecting money—as if there existed an unconscious understanding—as something bad and dirty. In many languages (language, art, and folklore are treasure chests in this regard) the words for "miserly" and "dirty" are the same. In English we have "filthy lucre," while the French say that "money does not smell," a reassurance which may seem startling and superfluous to the naïve person. In German, to say that "somebody is a dirty person" does not differentiate between whether he is unclean or miserly. We also find that there is a widespread inhibition with regard to money claims. There are a great many people in the world who cannot ask for money to which they are entitled without blushing and wishing that somebody else would handle this delicate problem for them. Thus, among professional people it has become the task of protective secretaries to take over this burden from their employers.

When the child's adjustment process—dependent upon the intensity of his drives, his push for activity, his urges toward mastery and independence, and the degree and quality of the environment's preoccupation with toilet training—leads to conflicts that are not sufficiently resolved, the struggle may become shifted from the original center of conflict to other areas. It might be transformed into stubborn belligerence as mentioned before, or warded off and submissively accepted by overregularity, overcleanliness, etc. In some cases almost every interest or habit belonging to this infantile situation may be repressed, except the struggle connected with it, the rebellion against being forced to adjust to the demands of the adult environment and to the schedule imposed upon the child. There may remain a special rebelliousness, a general resistance against any further regulations or commands in the form of an intense stubborness and willfulness. This struggle of the child for the right to his personal habits can lead to extraordinary hostility against the environment which deprives him of his ways of obtaining satisfaction and pleasure.

Another method of dealing with this problem can be by means of what we call a *reaction formation* or overcompensation, that is, an attempt to control undesirable impulses by firmly and rigidly holding them in check and by establishing opposite tendencies. In the case of the little boy who loved to torment cats, discussed in Lecture 1, the reaction formation might have led to preoccupation with fighting the cruelty in the world wherever it can be found. The reaction formation of persons with strong anal dispositions is found in the frequently observed overcleanliness, overorderliness, and overexactness, which may be expressed in almost hypochrondriacal reactions to anything dirty, messy, or smelly as dangerous and damaging to one's health. If we look closely, it is almost always possible to find within or next to these overcompensations the original impulses scarcely hidden.

For example, we all know certain women who have what we call the "housewife neurosis," which is more a character formation than a real neurotic disturbance; these women, who see their goal in life as being on their hands and knees all day trying to clean away dirt wherever they hope to find it, are both happily excited and seemingly annoyed when they discover a spot, and in the end always live in the dirt, preoccupied with it, and fighting it, never at leisure to enjoy the neatness that they have achieved. We also can see, which proves our point, that most people of this type find a special pleasure in cleaning or making order after they have permitted the mess to grow. Many of them cannot bring themselves to a more permanent, systematic cleanliness on a small scale, but find a way of living out their repressed tendencies in a camouflaged form. As in the case of a person who keeps his closet in a mess behind closed doors and cleans it up once a month, as a prelude to messing it up again, they first satisfy their original interest in dirt, then they fight it in one big effort, and then they start all over again from the beginning.

A special sense of responsibility and high standards go with the aforementioned cleanliness, exactness, and orderliness, resulting in a pervasive self-scrutiny. As a result, the conflict around dirt and disorder is shifted to problems of a higher order, involving ethics and orderly thinking. A type of overcorrectness, a highly developed, very vulnerable conscience, a brooding over right and wrong, and strong, very strict and rigid points of view seem to ward off or keep watch over those old sloppy, messy habits. The person carefully lives up to his responsibilities and ideals, and is disinclined to take things lightly, make compromises, or indulge in anything.

Next to these transformations, sublimations, reactions against and indirect continuations of the childhood impulses, you may discover in this type of person special toilet problems and habits, such as constipation or diarrhea, general worries about digestion, and ceremonial arrangements around elimination. For example, they may use the toilet only after breakfast or only after the first cigarette, and they are preoccupied with laxatives and healthy bowel functioning. These are people who will always know quite exactly every day whether they have moved their bowels and will have a definite opinion on the quality of this movement, as if all that the day will bring depended on its perfection. In contrast, the average person does not have to be aware of the details of his bowel activity and be preoccupied with it, yet it functions well.

As we enumerate all these different trends, which we see singly or in combination, they may seem somewhat incoherent. If we summarize them now, you will probably recognize a familiar kind of person, the type that is called the anal or compulsive personality: this person is often extraordinarily particular, has an inclination to collect and preserve possessions up to the point of being stingy, is very careful with money, somewhat stubborn, somewhat righteous, very ethical and strict toward himself and others, orderly, exact, systematic, always on time, concerned with outer and inner cleanliness, and always inclined to stand up for principles. He is clear-thinking and rational, and dislikes fuzziness. He is an excellent citizen, reliable and responsible. He may not always be an easy person to have fun with because of his reserve, his need to keep emotions well under control, or because he has little sense of humor, but frequently is endowed with biting sarcasm.

Although it might be unnecessary and repetitive, we would like to mention a few points which we have to keep in mind whenever we consider different personality types.

First, in our effort to clarify the nature of personalities we are forced to simplify a variety of complicated data. If we keep the perspective which should always accompany careful diagnostic procedure, we know that quick observations can be erroneous, that none of the problems under discussion is so clear-cut that we cannot make mistakes, and that none is so simple that it can always be explained from only one angle. There is a temptation for all of us, and especially for beginners in an interesting field, to generalize with inappropriate assurance from the first knowledge that we have gathered. But we can be sure that the more experience we have, the more cautious we become in our approach and diagnosis.

Secondly, we must remember that the instinctual basis of our adult personality formation does not depreciate the value of the latter. Growing up means using our instincts as a driving power, transforming them, and shifting and sublimating them. There is nothing disgraceful in the fact that many of our qualities can be traced back, with enough attention and knowledge, to elementary problems and experiences of our childhood. As our knowledge increases, so does our respect for the human struggle, the unceasing attempt through education, culture, and civilization to change into something less primitive, to be directed by other principles than simple physical needs and satisfactions.

A third point to bear in mind in our consideration of personality types is that they are by no means pathological conditions. The kinds of personalities that we are describing represent normal, stabilized modes of adjustment of people who will usually have definite assets and certain liabilities in coping with any given life situation. Of course, the intensification of conflicts under special situations of stress may, at any time, lead to a heightening of these character traits or even to personality disorders as well as to other forms of psychopathology.

Thus all the peculiarities which were mentioned before

may lead under especially difficult circumstances to the development of a neurotic disturbance, the obsessional or obsessive-compulsive neurosis. The obsessional neurotic patient suffers chiefly from strange compulsions to think filthy words, often of a blasphemous nature, or perform aggressive acts, usually concerning the people or things which are nearest to him or which he appreciates most. The patient feels forced against his will and as if by an external pressure to do or think certain things lest he suffer extreme tension. The obsessive urges or thoughts seem impersonal to the patient, often appearing without an appropriate degree of emotion, and as though they do not quite belong to him, yet they create great discomfort because of their compelling nature. He may think, "I will call out something nasty in church," or "I will want to insult my guests," though he has no conscious hostility or malicious intent. The symptom may take the form of compulsive fears: "Maybe I have committed a crime," or "I may have run over a person, I must stop my car and look," with the patient knowing fully at the same time that none of these urges or fears are real, but still he is unable to disregard them.

Another common symptom is that of compulsive doubting: "Did I turn off the gas, lock the door, or put out the fire?" The patient almost always fights these obsessions and compulsions with equally compulsive countermeasures; as a result, the original urge becomes obscured or vague, changes to a general anxiety regarding now meaningless or absurd words or actions; or the original thought will disappear completely and be replaced by the counterobsession. These countermeasures are what we usually meet first in our obsessional neurotic patients. They represent a system of symbolic protective activities directed against living out unconscious dirty or aggressive impulses. For instance, these patients complain that they have to wash their hands over and over again, feel impelled to count up to a certain number between two successive events, or find themselves forced to repeat seemingly senseless words, because otherwise something awful may happen: death in their family, national disaster, or a more vague catastrophe.

Dr. H., a patient of this kind, suffered from anxiety when he touched or pushed against something involuntarily. He could not explain this anxiety, but there was a distinct though absurd fear connected with it. He feared that this involuntary touch might, according to the physical law of conservation of energy, not come to a stop but spread around the world and finally hit someone delicate who might be harmed by it. Dr. H., a mathematician, was quite aware at the same time that his fears were absurd and irrational. Nevertheless, he had to prevent this possibility with an obsessional activity whose goal was to undo the harmful act. He had to touch the object under all circumstances again, with the corresponding other side of his body. However, as it almost invariably happens in an obsessional neurosis, this solution soon was not sufficient. After a short time his compulsions spread; he felt tempted to repeat the first touch, had to keep it in check by repeating the second one, and finally he came to treatment with the system of touching everything alternately three times with the right and three times with the left side, or vice versa on good days, or on very bad days, three times three (that is, nine times), touching with the right side and then the left side or vice versa.

We need not describe the life of an intelligent person ridden by such symptoms. In the analysis a childhood conflict centering around toilet training stood out. He was one of those children whose upbringing and training created special difficulties, and in his struggle with his beloved, but very strict nurse, he once in an outburst of rage and excitement tried to soil her on purpose by throwing his food (chicken a la king and spinach) upon her. The girl was very upset about it and within a short time, as far as he recalled, she left. He was convinced that she departed because of his misbehavior, and remembered being very unhappy about this and daydreaming of how to find her, of going out into the world to look for her. As he grew up he developed rather well and changed from the willful, sloppy, and aggressive child into a well-behaved young man. But sometimes when he was angry he would have fantasies of covering his room, the house, even the whole world with his feces. When he was eighteen he fell in love with a girl, a nursemaid as he reported (without his being aware of a possible connection between her job and that of his first love, his governess). After a short while he became anxious in the presence of this girl and discovered that he had difficulties in his sexual life; he was not quite potent or not quite interested, and then he slowly developed his obsessional symptoms. With the onset of symptoms he lost his respect for the girl, rejected her as low and inferior, and eventually severed their relationship.

It may not be too difficult to trace the unconscious meaning of his symptoms. The intimacy with his girlfriend, who was chosen after the image of his own governess, revived his old, repressed impulses of loving and at the same time provoking by attacking her, as he had done to his governess in childhood. Nothing of this memory of the early experiences entered his conscious mind at the time that his symptoms began. Nevertheless, he reacted to it in his neurosis with the concern that his touch would spread over the whole world and on its way meet somebody delicate who would be harmed by it, namely, his governess who in his view had shown so clearly that his aggressive, loving behavior could not be tolerated by her and would drive her away. He regarded making love (expressed in his wish to touch his girlfriend) as being dirty, leading to the terrifying unconscious conflict of wanting to touch the girl, that is, to dirty her, and believing that if he did so he would harm her. The symptoms of undoing his touch served the purpose of keeping in check his unconscious impulse to destroy, to soil, and to attack with his love. In giving way to a second, third, and sometimes ninth breakthrough of the impulse to touch he symbolically expressed these aggressive wishes, yet always carefully trying to undo, to blot out, to balance his initial intention.

Many of us may recognize in ourselves or others slight obsessional inclinations, and when we observe children on their way from school we notice how often such tendencies find their expression in superstitions and games. The children all seem to avoid or to be attracted by the cracks in the pavement and to touch every window or door that they pass. A. A. Milne (1924) has described this phenomenon charmingly in his poem, *Lines and Squares:*

> Whenever I walk in a London street,
> I am ever so careful to watch my feet;
>> And I keep in the squares,
>> And the masses of bears,
> Who wait at the corners all ready to eat,
> The sillies who tread on the lines of the street,
>> Go back to their lairs,
>> And I say to them, "Bears,
>> Just look how I'm walking in all of the squares!"

The element of aggressiveness, warded off in the game and represented by the threatening bears in the poem, is often expressed more directly by children who warn as they play: "Step on a crack and break your mother's back!"

It is important to remember that all of us really do have certain remainders of such early problems within us; we all had to cope with them and as a result have more or less deep scars. Many persons retain some of these childhood ceremonials like touching playfully and yet systematically all the windows on a block; however, they do not break down and are not overwhelmed by anxieties if they miss one of them. They can easily give up this game if something more interesting occupies their minds, or they find themselves doing it now and then without such an act ever becoming a compulsion. Similarly, we must remember that the compulsive personality type is a well-integrated, normal, and useful member of society. He is a reliable, careful, systematic, very hard-working and well-disciplined, ethical person, possessing qualities of great value.

You might want to know whether we can derive something from our increased understanding of this childhood period and its importance for later development, something that could help prevent the subsequent development of frank neurosis or of a more rigid, inhibited, and indecisive adult personality. It is not very easy to answer this question because the extent of the conflict is not always due to the amount of frustration by the parents or to the degree of traumatic punishment; but, as mentioned before, the outcome depends as well upon different given elements, especially the intensity of a child's impulses. That means, if the force of the instinctual drive is great and if it is combined with a special willfulness, the child has greater difficulty in modifying it and giving up its direct expression: the stronger the impulse, the less trauma is needed to form the nucleus for a fixation, i.e., the persistence of an infantile focus for specific character traits or for future neurotic disturbances.

Moreover, in all questions of training and upbringing there are dangers at two extremes: too great indulgence and too great frustration. Indulgence in the form of excessive stimulation leads to a persistence of the urge, in this case, for anal pleasure; this usually occurs as a result of the interest and activity of mothers and nursemaids who have the same unconscious problems to cope with in themselves. These people, who have persistent worries about the child's defecation, may overstimulate him through too frequent remarks about his excretion, through questioning, warning, and persuading, and through giving too much support in accomplishing bowel control by the means of enemas and cathartics.

Frustration is largely a consequence of the extremely rejecting and severely punishing attitude of the environment toward any lapse in toilet training or irregularity, and also toward all derivatives of soiling such as playing with mud or being sloppy in general: like the mother of a little boy who permitted him to eat only vanilla ice-cream cones, though he would much rather have had chocolate; she was afraid that he might get dirty and stain his clothes.

It is interesting to note that bowel functions are less of a general problem in cultures where later and less intense training is the rule. This observation may perhaps sound exaggerated, and yet it is meant quite seriously. In countries with strict toilet training such as England and the United States, until not too long ago, the problem of digestion had special significance. It results in the preoccupation with cathartics and deodorants which are openly and persistently advertised.

The issue is how to find a balance between restriction, not frustration, and permission rather than indulgence. For, too strict an attitude of the environment leads to violent, anxious repression of the impulse with all of the aforementioned consequences: fixation of the interest; the feeling of guilt in connection with it; the return of what has been repressed in the disguised form of neurotic symptoms. Uncontrolled indulgence works like a seduction, fostering or increasing the drive which finally must meet the full force of social criticism and rejection.

Mrs. E., a young professional woman, came very reluctantly for a consultation concerning her three-year-old son who was wild and unmanageable in nursery school. When asked whether there were other problems, she admitted that the boy was not toilet trained at all and still wore diapers. The mother's reluctant manner, her asking for help and yet being so hesitant, indicated that she was very much involved in the problem. She was one of the young modern women who had learned certain things about child rearing and accepted them without a genuine understanding of the child's needs. Her explanation for having omitted toilet training the child was the following: she worked half time, employing a baby-sitter for these hours; since she knew that toilet training was very important and had an effect on the future development of a child, she did not believe that this important job of training should be divided between two people. Thus the child was not trained and at the same time he was expected to adjust to a nursery school where soiling made him an outcast, which led to great unhappiness in the child and increasingly aggressive and destructive behavior on his part.

We might be able to keep away from extremes and to maintain the necessary balance if we avoid premature training and do not make these issues an object of fierce fight and struggle, but instead treat them with calmness as we would anything else in the child's upbringing, such as his dressing, learning to clean his teeth, or going to sleep at night, and if we proceed slowly with a not too vigorous toilet-training program, show patience and give friendly praise when the child succeeds. In addition to reasonable permissiveness and limit setting, when a child shows difficulties in shifting his attention from the excretory functions, we try to offer him more appropriate, socially acceptable substitutes for his tendencies; that is, we help him sublimate them. We can facilitate what the child at this age normally does spontaneously, if he is permitted to do so, by introducing him to painting, especially finger painting, and play with clay, sand, or mud pies.

A brief illustration of the intelligent handling of a child who had already developed some symptoms of obsessional neurosis as well as features of compulsive personality structure will lead us to the important area of the medical management of the adult of this type (Bergmann, 1937). Lisa, a ten-year-old girl, would not begin to learn to write and her well-trained teacher discovered that she did not want to spoil the beautiful, clean, white sheet of paper before her with pencil marks. Accordingly, the teacher squared the paper very neatly and asked Lisa to put each letter into a square, showing her how to do it in an orderly and systematic way. That is, the teacher took into account the girl's concern with cleanliness and the taboo of touching: she emphasized neatness and the separateness of the letters by having the child carefully write in the blocks ("Lines and Squares!"). Then she asked Lisa to transfer these same letters to paper which was only lined horizontally, and finally she had her write on a sheet which was not lined at all. She succeeded because she understood the youngster's psychological system and tried to direct it in a constructive way rather than to break it, i.e., she recognized the child's behavior as the outcome of an internal struggle against old, objectionable impulses to soil herself by handling dirty things. The child had contained this struggle by holding down these impulses through the reaction formation of overneatness and overcleanliness. In directing Lisa step by step from a neat pattern of letters separated by squares to a neat, coherent line of letters, and then to the freedom of writing on clean paper without fear of disturbing it, Bergmann freed the child's writing from involvement in an unconscious struggle.

How then do we proceed in the medical care of the adult patient who has an obsessive-compulsive personality structure? How do we take into account and meet his psychological needs?

Mr. F., a fifty-year-old musician, had been hospitalized because of a malignancy, requiring an operation with removal of a part of his large bowel followed by the creation of a colostomy. Psychiatric consultation was requested because the patient, after his operation, developed depressive reactions which seemed alarming to the doctors. He was described by the resident as a difficult patient who, all through his hospital stay, had created many scenes and conflicts with the environment, especially the professional staff, by making innumerable, persistent complaints. He protested that the ventilation was bad, constantly tried to open the windows, and one of his major concerns was the disorderly condition of the bathrooms on the ward. He frequently informed the nurses that he was writing a critical letter to the director of the hospital.

In the psychiatric interview it was found that Mr. F.'s preoccupation with neatness and cleanliness and the rigidity of his requests in this direction were not restricted to his experiences in the hospital. For instance, he told us quite frankly that his life was difficult because of certain professional problems that he encountered. As a musician he had played in some of the best orchestras in the United States, but there had been a constant downward movement with regard to his employment from orchestras of highest standing to those of lower rank because, as he was told by conductors, of his excessive formality and the lack of freedom in his performance. They all appreciated his devotion and careful work but were disappointed by the absence of any imaginative spark. The patient admitted that in spite of his love for music and his obvious gift for it, he was himself aware of a certain rigidity and formalization which always interfered with his creative musicianship. His wife complained about similar problems with him which led to great difficulties over small items at home. For example, he was utterly intolerant of little irregularities and slipups in household matters which he expected to be faultlessly to his liking. His wife said that she could produce an intense storm if the breakfast toast deviated in the slightest from the shade that he personally preferred, if it was a bit overdone or underdone.

The psychiatrist who saw this patient for the first time in a conference with house officers asked Mr. F. whether he was a man who balanced his checkbook, and the patient answered with conviction, "Up to the last cent." The question was asked to test a diagnostic impression that the patient's attitudes, virtues, and difficulties belonged in all likelihood to the compulsive personality type. The interview, therefore, went more specifically in this direction, and a number of confirmations were found in the patient's history and in his relationships with people. The patient's response to his operation was in keeping with these findings. He was especially burdened by the colostomy, which for a person of his exactness, regularity, and rigid neatness created an unacceptable threat. In talking about his concern he told the psychiatrist that he felt extremely depressed with the idea of his now being utterly messy, smelly, and irregular; he simply could not see himself existing under conditions which were so much opposed to his nature, were so much against all he stood for and found acceptable in living. This deep distress was taken into consideration when attempts were made to set up a medical-psychological management and rehabilitation for the patient.

It was decided to concentrate definitely on all the planning and activities connected with the care of his most offensive condition, the colostomy. In keeping with what we had learned from Mr. F. as to the way he handled his life in general, the emphasis was placed upon how he could become regulated in spite of his very distressing condition—how he could again become clean and in control of his functions. A great deal of time was spent on discussing with him the ways and means by which to master and regulate a colostomy, until the patient finally discovered that he could be one of the people who are able to achieve cleanliness and control in spite of a crucial handicap. He developed a keen interest in different diets, discussed with his doctors the effects of diet upon digestion, and was curious about the time that various foods needed in order to be eliminated. Soon his depression lifted and his dissatisfaction lessened as he became an expert in dealing with his disability.

To summarize the principles of psychological management: under the stress of illness, a patient of this type presents specific problems. Illness affects his equilibrium not only by threatening his life and activities, by interfering seriously with his need for independence and full control over his own affairs, by creating pain and exhaustion, or by fostering regression, but also in a special way by interrupting the daily routines that form part of his system. Thus it menaces his ascendancy over repressed impulses of aggressiveness, untidiness, and self-indulgence. The reinforcement of his characteristic attitudes can be understood as a redoubled effort to keep these tendencies in check. All this makes him appear more stubborn than the average patient, somewhat self-righteous and rigid, demanding to know all the details and to remain in control of his medical care. However, it is exactly these tendencies which can be used constructively by the doctor, inviting his active cooperation and giving him as much information about his illness as is necessary for his rational understanding of the disease and its treatment.

Sexual Differentiation: The Oedipus Complex and Its Resolution

Depending in some measure upon how satisfactorily the problems of the preceding period were settled, the child has now acquired control over his body functions and an increasing variety of motor, linguistic, and intellectual skills. He is more or less ready to approach a wider area of family and social relationships.

From about three to five years of age the child shows a growing interest in the world and slowly learns to understand it. He asks questions about practically everything, some of which, concerning abstract concepts, are difficult to answer: "Where does the snow come from?" "Why does it get dark at night?" "What is a distance? Can you see it? Does it stand there like a church?" Everything is noticed, becomes a problem, and finally may emerge as a question.

The child soon discovers that among the different topics that elicit this curiosity there is one that seems to have a different position—sex. Only rarely will such quite natural questions as those about the origin of babies be answered in the usual way and to their full extent, and even in these exceptional instances something secretive remains: they shouldn't know all the details, or they shouldn't talk about it to strangers; and mostly the child feels clearly the discomfort of the adults in speaking of things which seem to embarrass them. Therefore, from the beginning, sexuality has for most children in our culture something unclear, slightly improper about it, especially if the parents themselves are inhibited and disturbed in these matters. In some measure as a consequence the child creates a whole series of partly exciting, partly anxious fantasies often associated with the closed door of the parents' bedroom or with the birth of the next sibling.

Even though almost from the very beginning of their lives we observe definite differences in the ways that little boys and little girls behave and relate to the environment, in the main the psychological development of boys and girls is approximately parallel until this period. Both are chiefly attached to their mother, loving her almost exclusively, wanting to be with her, and they assure her that they will always stay with her. Their interest in father has been partly warm and friendly, partly disturbed by a certain rivalry: one likes him all right, but it is hard because whenever he comes home one takes second place with mother. Still, the competitive feeling has not been strong enough to lead to real tension. But at this time a new factor enters into the picture: the first manifestations of early, distinctly genital sexual responses.

This beginning genital drive is the forerunner of the extensive physiological transformation that sets in at puberty. In combination with his general curiosity, it leads the child to an intense interest in his own body and the discovery of his genital organ as a noteworthy part of his body, a part that has particular qualities and produces special sensations. This introduces for the first time the more systematic genital play of this period. Childhood masturbation arouses a certain pleasurable excitement, not yet any real sexual satisfaction. The child's discovery of his sex organ then broadens to the amazing problem of sexual differences: "What are boys and girls?" "What are women?" "What are men?" And something occurs that is of enormous importance. The children grasp for the first time fully that they are not alike. It is very interesting to observe that children who have certainly had the opportunity to notice the fact previously have not taken it in, have not accepted it, or have found it meaningless before this phase. But now they almost invariably recognize and notice it, either at home or with animals in the country or when they see a playmate urinate. A very important differentiation in the psychological development of the male and female child starts with this discovery.

To continue with the further development of the boy, which is in some ways simpler than that of the girl: his pleasurable interest in his genital organ and his curiosity about sexual matters lead to a new attitude toward little girls, and toward his parents and himself. This new attitude is reflected in his interests and behavior. It is not easy for him to comprehend the fact of biological sexual differences, that there are people who do not have genitals as he knows them. He begins to wonder what has happened, whether the girl has lost something. Through psychoanalysis we find that in many men this original rationalization of their sexual discovery, the idea that girls had the same kind of genitals as boys have but lost them, has persisted unconsciously and is represented by a basic conviction that there is something wrong with women, that they are missing something.

At this time the boy's relationship to his mother changes and his wish to be taken care of by her acquires a childlike erotic quality. We observe numerous examples of the boy's attitude ranging from his expressed wish, "When I grow up I will marry mother," or his question, "Why can't I sleep with you, and Daddy will sleep in my bed?" to attempts to caress his mother the way he has seen his father do it. The boy is very serious in this, as childish as it is judged from the adult point of view. The more the boy's attachment to his mother grows in this period, the more it complicates his relationship to his father.

Father does not remain the peripheral figure in the background of the child's world, a friendly playmate who seems sometimes a little irritable and less approachable than mother, but he now becomes a distinct factor for the boy and a problem for him. The boy loves and admires father increasingly as the ideal of what he wants to become himself. But simultaneously, opposite feelings interfere with this—rivalry, envy, and hostility toward the more successful competitor. Such a struggle between positive and negative feelings is what we call *ambivalence*. It would perhaps be simpler in a certain way if the boy could just dislike his opponent, though normally he could not hope for much success in this struggle with his father. The result would probably be disappointment, perhaps persistent rebelliousness, complete resignation, or a combination of these. However, the admixture of positive feelings to these competitive, hostile strivings causes discomfort and guilt in the child, provokes anxiety and fears of punishment, and finally leads to apprehensive concern with the organ that has such significance in these fantasies, the boy's genitals. This concern manifests itself in a variety of fears such as that the penis might stay small and weak and never become as big and powerful as that of a man—of father —or that it might be damaged by father; it might even be cut off or taken away, as it must have happened to the girls.

We see signs of this conflict in every civilization, in laws directed against boys' wishes regarding their mothers. In primitive societies they are expressed in initiation rites, where the struggle between the generation of the fathers and of the sons is represented in the symbolic form of a ceremonial cutting or scratching or wounding of the penis of the maturing boy by an older man before the boy is permitted to take up sexual contact with women. The meaning of these ceremonies and prohibitions was discussed by Freud in his book, *Totem and Taboo* (1913). They constitute the warning of the fathers to their young rivals based upon unconscious jealousy, and the submission of the boys to their fathers' threat, the boys' promise to keep the expression of their sexual and aggressive wishes within permitted boundaries and to accept punishment if they transgress. The same theme of incestuous wishes, guilt, and punishment underlies the ancient myth and drama of King Oedipus of Thebes. Though this legend is well known, it may be important in this context to repeat some of its details.

When Oedipus was born, his parents, Laius and Jocasta, King and Queen of Thebes, got word from an oracle that their son would slay his father. The unhappy parents decided to kill the child and left him to die in the wild mountain region of Cithaeron. A shepherd found him and brought him to his master and mistress in Corinth, where Oedipus grew up as their child. When he was a young man he too was told by the oracle of Delphi that he would become the slayer of his father and wed his mother. Believing his foster parents to be his true parents, he left for the wide world in order to avoid this fate. On this flight Oedipus met an old man with his servants who did not let him pass politely. In the ensuing fight he killed the man, not knowing that this man was his father Laius, King of Thebes. Wandering further toward Thebes, Oedipus heard the story of the Sphinx sitting in front of the city, killing every traveler who could not solve the riddle that she was asking: "What is it that in the morning goes on four feet, at noon on two, and in the evening on three?" Oedipus succeeded in this task and destroyed the monster, and the people of Thebes expressed their gratitude by making him King and giving him as his wife the Queen Jocasta. Years later Thebes was afflicted with famine and plague, the earth did not bear crops, and humans and animals failed to bear children. The cause of the disaster was again revealed by an oracle: it was the outrage committed by Oedipus, who killed his father and married his mother. Oedipus in his horror punished himself by piercing his eyes and leaving his home for an exile in the wilderness as a blind man.

Freud saw in this myth the expression of the central

conflict of the son in the developmental period that we are now discussing, and called the constellation of the child's problems the *oedipus complex*. Many of the elements which we referred to stand out clearly in the story. The riddle of the Sphinx alludes to "the ages of man" and thus bears elliptically upon his nature (and origin) and belongs to the childhood age of questioning. The influence of a sense of guilt is depicted in Oedipus's self-inflicted punishment: the oracle that acts as the emissary of the gods is like an embodiment of the relentless voice of conscience. That the punishment, like the crime, should be so drastic is in keeping with the intense fantasies of the young child. As you know, severe and retaliatory penalties are also a typical feature of ancient and primitive codes of law. It was Freud's inference that the genitals were displaced by an equally vital part of the body, the eyes. We call the dread of being damaged physically, a punishment connected with the oedipus complex, *castration* or *mutilation fear*.

A neurotic symptom that originated in this conflict and appeared later in life was observed in the case of a young man, Mark G., who suffered from attacks of anxiety whenever he saw a dangerous instrument. Mark had the phobic dread that if he handled knives, guns, or razor blades, he would damage his eyes with them. He had grown up as the youngest and physically weakest child among a number of older brothers in his father's logging camp. From early childhood on he was a withdrawn, avidly reading, and intellectual youngster, in contrast to the men of his group who were active in hunting, fishing, and tree felling. The boy used to hide in the cabin when the men left for work, staying behind with his mother and his books.

This behavior was fought angrily by his father who, when Mark was an adolescent, one day dragged him out of the cabin and forced an axe into his hands, ordering him to chop wood. As the boy lifted his axe in a wave of rage, he suddenly had the urge to split open his father's head. He dropped the axe in horror and then, in short succession, fears of axes, fears of kitchen knives and other dangerous instruments appeared, but with the idea that he might damage his eyes with one of these tools.

We see in this abbreviated case material a relatively simply structured neurotic development from which we can extrapolate clearly the underlying unconscious conflict. It seems that the resentment of the boy against his forceful father, who interfered with his wish to stay close to mother and pursue his interest in reading and learning, evoked an intense destructive hostility. This impulsive rage was followed by severe anxiety that these dangerous instruments, his father's and the men's tools, would turn against him and punish him by destroying his precious organ, his searching eyes which were his major tool in pursuing his own life in opposition to his father. This case is noteworthy because of its striking similarity to the punishment which befell Oedipus. In such cases of phobia beginning at puberty and later, as we have illustrated, the fear of being attacked or mutilated appears as the main or only indication of the unconscious aggressive impulse directed against the father, based on sexual rivalry, and unconsciously regarded as an accomplished crime for which there must be a punishment in the persistent childhood way of thinking. The conflict has been symbolically displaced from the genitals to another part of the body (the eyes), and concentrates upon the dangerous tools (the knives, etc.) which have to be avoided.

The little boy's tendency to feel guilty and to imagine dangers when involved in his sexual interests is often increased by direct or indirect threats made by the parents in their reaction to the child's masturbation. When a father makes up his mind to talk to his boy about sex, there is still a tendency for him to concentrate frequently on the "bad habits" (masturbation) or venereal diseases. Interestingly enough, without being aware of it, he will repeat what he had listened to with panic in his own boyhood: that masturbation or intercourse is basically bad or sinful or dangerous, that it makes you sick or weak or damages you. Even when the boy has more understanding parents who do not threaten in this fashion, he may hear and in a certain way believe the worst of everything he is told by anybody. The forbidden, incestuous, and aggressive fantasies accompanying the sexual feelings at this age frequently remain linked up with masturbation and therefore tend to render it extremely evil. Phobic reactions, nightmares, and fears of bodily injury occur as a result.

In adolescence the frightening ideas about the consequences of masturbation are a frequent cause of learning difficulties, in addition to that mentioned previously, namely, feeding problems. The children are inclined to believe that their brains have been damaged, softened, or drained by these "bad" activities, and they cannot hope to function normally. They accompany their studies with an incessant, anxious observation, finding all kinds of symptoms as results of the imagined lesion, like lack of memory, difficulty in concentrating, and so on. Under these conditions they are not aware of the fact that originally their anxiety created the difficulty in studying; rather, they believe that it is the difficulty which creates their anxiety.

Among other expressions of the same problem and fear are psychogenic symptoms of weakness, tiredness, tension headaches, and backaches. A certain type of sleeplessness may be created by this conflict, due to the struggle against the temptation to masturbate, which emerges at bedtime. Hypochondriacal self-observation may occur, with anxious concentration upon the expected signs and symptoms in one's appearance like pallor, circles under the eyes, and lines in his face. In some cases this general anxiety turns into a fixed idea, so that what has been expected fearfully becomes a rigidly established conviction of physical defects. These ideas will often be associated with organs that represent something especially essential such as the eyes, or with a part of the body such as the nose or the ear which, by its shape, is fit to serve as a symbolic substitute for the genitals. Or the *idée fixe* may center on any organ that shows the most minute imperfection, which is then perceived as an extreme and most conspicuous abnormality.

Eric, a seventeen-year-old, handsome boy, was tormented by a completely irrational conviction: he suffered from the misapprehension that his ears stuck out to such a degree that people found him ugly and unpleasant to look at. It did not help him at all that his family tried to convince him of the opposite, that he was very successful in his relationships with friends, and that surgeons whom he consulted refused to operate on him, after they had taken measurements proving that his ears were within the range of normal. He could not take comfort even in the friendliness that girls showed toward him. Whenever events contradicted his troubled convictions, he always found plausible reasons to disregard this evidence: "Parents never see faults in their own children," he said; "The surgeons are influenced by my family"; and "Girls always want to be nice and try not to hurt a guy." For a time he had attempted to tape back his ears. He finally trained himself to wiggle his ears and to hold them back by muscular control when in the presence of others.

It was impressive to observe his efforts, which kept him under a steady strain without being objectively justified and without even having a discernible effect. Moreover, this kind of achievement did not solve his inner conflict. Instead of feeling freed of his anxiety he developed a hypochondriacal fear that by pulling his ears in this way he strained the muscles of his scalp and thus stopped the blood supply, which sooner or later was bound to lead to baldness—baldness had the same unconscious significance as his concern about his ears. The interesting part was that concurrently he knew somewhere that his ideas were fantastic, that his ears objectively were all right, and that he didn't really change their position significantly by his muscular stunt. Nevertheless, he could not rid himself of the troubled feeling that something was profoundly wrong with him. Further discussions led us back from the boy's symptoms to the intense underlying struggle against masturbation and to his father's warnings in puberty concerning the destructive nature of masturbation.

The question of masturbation and its effect is frequently brought to the doctor for his explanation and advice. Are there any deleterious consequences? Certainly not those which popular beliefs attribute to it. A person's physical energy will not be depleted by it. His brains will not be stunted. No diseases are brought about by masturbation. In general, we must say that its main function is to serve as an outlet for sexual tensions that cannot be relieved in direct activity and cannot be sufficiently discharged in substitute activities, e.g., intensive interests and work. But there is the possibility that certain problems may be created by it. The most important is the very frequent feeling of guilt that results from masturbation. Even when threatening remarks to the child are avoided, as is more and more the case nowadays, there still remains an inclination in almost every child and adult to expect some harm to come from it: because, for the child, sexual activity is always connected with early incestuous and aggressive fantasies which lead to vague apprehensions of its being bad and forbidden; sex is almost invariably surrounded by an atmosphere of secrecy, and parents react with some sign of disapproval whenever they perceive the child's masturbatory activities. Furthermore, after the discovery of the difference between the sexes, this fear is reinforced by the childlike conviction that one can lose one's genital organ. This fear can be so real for the child that it may prove difficult to reassure him fully.

Berta Bornstein, a psychoanalyst with great experience in the treatment of children, reported the following: at a vacation resort she was asked by a mother to talk to her five-year-old boy about these problems. The mother had observed that the child was masturbating secretly and at the same time had become shy, oversensitive, and anxious, which suggested to her that he felt he was doing something wrong. The therapist went on a walk with the boy, discussed many things with him, and finally arrived at the question of his masturbation. The boy appeared to be waiting for her opinion on the matter and she reassured him that most boys do that at his age, that he should not worry, and that nobody was angry with him about it.

One year later she again met the boy, who was then six, at the same resort. He recognized her and she asked him casually whether he remembered the talk they had had a year ago. "Yes," he said, thinking hard. "Can you remember what we talked about?" "I don't know," said the boy, "but I think we saw something, a piece of glass or a wire and you said I should be careful not to step on it or it will cut me." Thus the child revealed that he had repressed the memory of the episode and what remained was a fear of injuring himself by his "vice." You can see how the therapist's remarks did not influence the child's anxious expectation that he will be injured as a consequence of masturbating. He remembered the therapist as warning him instead of reassuring him. The piece of glass or wire, which he might have seen during their walk, represented the unconscious content of his fears, as a punishing, cutting instrument.

Masturbation may have another ill effect in the case of anxious and insecure children who prefer to avoid tasks, struggles, and any possible failures, and for these reasons content themselves with substitute gratifications: for them, masturbation, like thumb sucking, represents a pitfall, a regular replacement, and should be looked upon as a problem similar to any habitual escape mechanism. As with other self-protective but self-limiting habits, such as avoiding sports because of fear of competition, or staying away from children's parties because of fear of being rejected, these signs of insecurity should be heeded. The child must not be forced to overcome them, but rather his self-confidence should be strengthened. This can be achieved by guiding him, starting with what he is capable of doing and helping him slowly, without pressure to solve more difficult tasks, until he recognizes that he can be successful and that he is liked and accepted.

We have depicted the boy's first erotically tinged attachment to his mother, and his rivalry with his loved, admired, and feared father, against whom he cannot succeed. We mentioned among the immediate and future consequences of this conflict the establishment of fears around masturbation and the possible appearance of certain symptoms; in Lecture 9 we shall consider further how the solution of this conflict may affect the shaping of the future pattern of his relationship to women. The common method of solving this problem is by repression, which contributes largely to the considerable amnesia that most grownups have for the early years of life. Repression has to be understood as an essential and successful method of solving developmental conflicts, and only under unfavorable conditions does it play a major part in the unsuccessful solutions leading to psychopathology.

When the boy, prompted by the fear of mutilation, has to give up his intense, conflicting, incestuous, and aggressive impulses toward mother and father, he at the same time seems to identify with his parents more strongly and in a special way. Since early infancy the child's personality has been progressively enriched by imitating and identifying with his parents and other important figures. To a certain extent he has acquired skills, language, mannerisms, interests, and many other attributes and qualities in this fashion. This same process of becoming like another person may be initiated when anyone, child or adult, loses or must relinquish that person. It may also become operative in situations of insurmountable conflict when, if you cannot defeat your adversary, you "join him." For the boy, it is as if by being like his parents, by acquiring their attitudes toward his impulses, he can move into their position and with it also enjoy their privileges, which of course will one day be true.

As a result, for the first time, the parents' and especially the father's demands and prohibitions will be seriously accepted by the child, representing an inner force that we call his *superego*. This superego then comprises his conscience as well as the ideals toward which he is striving. A tendency may persist to maintain the figure of his father as the model of formidable power throughout the rest of his life. It may become the image of authority and this quality may be transferred to any figure in a similar position. The boy's future relationship to teachers, counselors, bosses, and officials will bear the signs of his attitude toward his father in this childhood period, and of the ways in which he reached a resolution of this conflict.

After the establishment of the child's major identifications, his superego becomes increasingly stabilized. It will be modified by new identifications during adolescence. Changing the structure of the superego becomes increasingly difficult in later life, yet with a certain youthful quality of the individual his superego remains flexible and continues to develop. Some people never stop growing under the impact of major relationships and responsibilities, notwithstanding that the core of the superego remains linked with the experiences of the oedipal period.

The boy's relationship to his mother also undergoes some changes at this time. It loses its erotic quality, and only fondness and affection remain. Masturbation diminishes or disappears completely. With a readiness and hunger for learning, for intellectual activity, and for pursuing his many interests, with an urge to become a strong, nice, competent, and good person, a completely new chapter in the child's life begins. We shall consider this phase, called the *latency period*, after we have given thought to the psychological development of the girl.

To go back to those events surrounding the meaningful discovery of the anatomical differences between the sexes, we can observe that the *girl's* first reaction to this discovery is almost always one of disappointment with her own condition. It seems difficult for her to accept it; she may express indignation, unhappiness, and jealousy; she may deny the difference and cling to the idea that boys and girls are alike.

To explain this rather typical reaction a number of factors must be considered. One is that every child wants to have whatever others possess and do. The realization of the inevitable disparity and its acceptance with reasonable contentment are late results of the painful process of education. And it may be this simple fact of difference that creates the first—sometimes dramatic—reactions. The boy has something more, and the girl is envious of it. Her envy is based on the wish to be as complete as possible, a wish found in every human being, children as well as adults, regardless of whether this is truly advantageous or not.

Another possibility is that the girl's grievance may result from a certain environmental attitude. Many families openly treasure the boy as the one who will perpetuate the family name and tradition, and this overt appreciation is often accompanied by a somewhat depreciative condescension toward the girl. Furthermore, there is a basic tendency for a parent to choose the child of the opposite sex as the favored one. Thus when there are boys and girls in the family, the mother may be drawn more closely to her little son than to her girl. This has its special impact on the children because mother is the most important figure for them during their first years. Although the mother may be completely unaware of her preference, we can be sure that her observant little daughter, helped by the everpresent competitiveness in children, will sense and react to it. With this goes the fact that the behavior of boys has more attraction for children of this age, with their strong impulses and urges toward action. Not infrequently, little girls are admonished to behave properly when boys are not.

Finally, in connection with childhood masturbation and the environment's disapproval, the girl too associates a feeling of guilt with her sexual activities. She too wonders with a vague uneasiness whether she has damaged her genital organ, whether she has mutilated it by her own fault. It is very difficult for a child of this age to imagine and understand that she is different for biological reasons. The idea that she has become different from the boy by an accident or as a punishment, that she has lost her organ, whereas he has kept his, and that her genital organ is not an entity of its own but a wound—these ideas are more in keeping with the way children think at this stage. Such beliefs are not easily changed by realistic explanations because all that the parents can do is to point out the future function of her sex organs; to the child, who thinks concretely and has a limited tolerance for delay, this is neither fully comprehensible nor does it represent any acceptable compensation.

Ordinarily when a child of this age feels hurt he turns to his parents, especially to the mother, for help and recompense. With the increasing discovery that mother does not help in this instance, a certain grudge and distrust of mother arises in the girl: it just does not seem possible to understand that mother really did her best and that what appears to be a bodily deficiency to the child is neither an actual defect nor proof of mother's negligence or lack of interest. Normally the way the girl solves these conflicts through the course of her develpoment is rather complex compared with that of the boy. She moves away from the intense attachment to her mother, her first and most important love object, and turns more to her father, with some resignation and with newly oriented hopes. With it she relinquishes her former boyish expectations and slowly replaces these by identification with her mother as a woman. She cannot insist any longer on becoming like her father or brother and on staying with her mother forever. And only then can she begin to talk about marrying father when she is grown up, about having babies and being a housewife.

This, then, is the usual solution of the girl's conflict: it is the regular step toward her future biological function. It is the step which leads away from the strong attachment of infancy to her mother. Thus she can accept her female body without much resentment, accept the female role and the reward—the baby—as true compensation, and she can choose a man, usually related to the image of her father. The girl thus changes her main love object, a change which has no regular parallel in the development of the boy. This experience will have its influence, through it may be only a very subtle one, upon her future relationships with men and women. Although she has redirected her love from the woman to the man, the girl tends to preserve within herself the traces of her first and most vital attachment to her mother. In her superego the predominant identification is with her mother, and she accepts the mother's commandments and prohibitions as binding.[1]

[1] In the early psychoanalytic literature the term introduced to designate the constellation of the girl's conflicts in this phase was *Electra complex*. It refers to another Greek legend in which Electra persuaded her brother to kill their mother, Clytemnestra, in retaliation for her infidelity and for her and her lover's crime of murdering their father, Agamemnon. Yet, the term Electra complex was never widely used, and oedipus complex is applied to the description of this developmental phase in both boys and girls.

6

Sexual Differentiation: Neurosis, Personality, and Medical Management

Perhaps the girl's more involved course of maturation is reflected in the fact that women are more prone than men to develop the form of neurosis known as hysteria, associated with the problems of this period, especially with the sexual taboos. Hysteria is a type of disturbance that usually comes to the attention of doctors as a diagnostic and a management problem when a patient presents complaints of a physical nature, without corresponding organic findings in the total examination. As hysterical mechanisms underlie a variety of psychological disturbances, and lie on the borderline between the medical and psychiatric areas, we believe it to be essential and appropriate to discuss the phenomena of this entire syndrome in all its details. In addition to bodily symptoms, hysterical disorders include certain fears, intellectual disturbances, and behavioral reactions; they all have in common certain dramatic and histrionic qualities. Just as there is no somatic disease causing the physical symptoms, there is no external danger justifying the fears, and no gross mental derangement responsible for the intellectual disturbances.

We shall try to outline and group the variety of hysterical symptoms, and to provide some clearer understanding of today's theoretical concepts as to the etiology of hysteria. And with it we may comprehend the common denominator behind these seemingly unconnected, unrelated peculiarities. Otherwise hysteria can become rather bewildering and confusing because of its diverse symptomatology. You may be alert to its symptoms in the course of taking the patient's anamnesis as you become aware of the intensity or the dramatic nature of the complaints—often incompatible with each other and sometimes expressed in a form which slowly awakens your doubts and suspicions as to the "validity" of the ailment. Or during the physical examination, observing certain motor functions or testing the sensory system, you may be impressed by the shifting, inconsistent, and clearly unreliable reactions and answers of the patient. This frequently leaves the examiner with the feeling that this behavior is consciously contrived; thus, it provokes irritation against the patient or the tendency to drop him as a nuisance. Don't! Instead try and understand the very meaningful ways in which hysterical symptoms come about. Let us first look at the overall picture of this neurosis which, heterogeneous as it may seem, nevertheless can be understood as the result of a common underlying problem.

1. *Anxiety hysteria or hysterical phobia* is characterized by excessive fears of situations, objects, or activities which in themselves need not be truly dangerous. The objects of anxiety are varied and anything that exists in the world or in one's imagination can become the center of fear, which might reach the proportions of a panic. The circumstances feared include such situations as closed or open spaces, heights or depths, traveling, and being in one's house or being outside of the house. Thus, being on mountains or on bridges, in tunnels or in railways, in elevators or airplanes, can be frightening. Fear of illness often concerns cancer, heart disease, disease of the brain, diabetes, vomiting or fainting, and operations or hypodermic injections. Animals that are feared might be

mice, cats, dogs, cows, horses, lions, frogs, snakes, spiders, moths, caterpillars, fish, and many others. When the content of the phobia is "being attacked," the patient may fear burglars, foreigners, or gypsies, dentists or doctors, ghosts, or, in the case of some women, men in general. Other common forms of phobia concern examinations, public speaking, thunderstorms, strange or loud noises, crowds, lonely places, forests, cemeteries, darkness, and nighttime. Usually, the fear is so intense that the patient feels compelled to take certain countermeasures: avoidance of the object of his fear is essential; he may keep a night-light burning, lock doors, or require that he always be accompanied by someone. The patient is aware of the fact that his fears are irrational. For example, in spite of the thought that he will faint, vomit, or even die if he should walk across an open square alone, he knows that he is actually in good physical health. The choice of the object of the phobia is principally determined by its fitness to represent certain frightening but unconscious ideas. When you consider the great variety of phobias, it must occur to you that probably everyone experiences some form of it in the course of time. In childhood, particularly when the oedipal conflict is at its height, mild and transitory phobias are almost universal.

2. *Conversion hysteria:* the symptoms resemble a physical condition, but do not necessarily coincide anatomically and physiologically with the elements that are found in an organic lesion. As the expression of an unconscious fantasy, the conversion symptom follows the patient's imagined, usually naïve, ideas of a physical process. A paralysis may involve an activity, such as walking, rather than follow the anatomical distribution of innervation. The dysfunction tends to be extravagant (e.g., extreme flaccidity of an entire limb) and at the same time sharply limited (a monoplegia) in a way that is not consistent with organic pathology. Similarly, a sensory deficit will be total in one area (e.g., sleeve anesthesia), stopping abruptly

where a true lesion would not be sharply demarcated. When a hysterical symptom appears after an injury, it may be out of proportion to the physical trauma: for example, immobilization of a leg following the bruising of a toe. The symptom may take the form of an apparent persistence of the normal physiological reactions to anxiety, shock, or strain, like headaches, palpitations, or feelings of weakness or nausea; these do not pass, but remain as the constant sensation of a ring pressing around the temples, as dizziness, paralysis, or the feeling of a globe in the throat. The symptom may affect various parts or systems in the body.

Motor and sensory elements of the nervous system may show hysterical involvement like paralyses, difficulties in standing and walking, unusual movements, tremors, convulsions, spasms and contractions, anesthesias, analgesias, paresthesias and pains, constricted vision, blindness, deafness, dizziness, and disturbance of taste and smell. Vasomotor manifestations include urticaria and hives, flushing, perspiration, coldness, and fainting. In the gastrointestinal system we observe nausea, vomiting, indigestion, abdominal bloating or pains, constipation, and diarrhea. Respiration may be interfered with by choking, or there may be coughing, dyspnea, sighing, hoarseness, stammering or mutism. Cardiac involvement may take the form of palpitations or pseudoangina. Genitourinary dysfunctions include impotence, frigidity, pseudocyesis, and urinary frequency or retention.

The multitude of possible manifestations (like the infinite variety of phobic situations) depends, so to speak, upon the details of what the patient is unconsciously trying to express. For example, a young girl developed a paralysis of her eye movements in which she was unable to look to the left. There was no organic basis for this disturbance. She had had a traumatic experience which coincided with the onset of the symptom. The patient had entered a room in her home and found her brother together with his girlfriend in an embrace on the couch, which to the patient was highly embarrassing as well as exciting. The symptom meant that she must not look to the left, the direction in which she had observed her brother, lest forbidden fantasies and feelings be aroused.

A special feature that is almost always present in conversion hysteria, and one that provides a clue to the clinical diagnosis, is a discrepancy between the extent of the symptomatic condition and the observable emotional reaction to it: the patient complains too much about a minor lesion, or might show a kind of serenity despite years of seemingly disabling paralysis; most typical is a relative lack of anxiety and concern about these "serious afflictions." The term *conversion* refers to an older concept in which anxiety is directly, almost physiologically, converted into the physical expression of a symptom. The patient's unconcern (*la belle indifference*) is in contrast to the concern of the organically ill person, the physical preoccupation of the hypochondriac, or the concentration of the malingerer on his alleged organic ailment.

It is important to note that hysterical patients are frequently suggestible and willing to please the examining doctor. Hence, if a patient has perfect vision when you first test it, you might find it quite impaired on your next examination, as if he obliged you with the symptoms once he understood what kind of disability you were trying to test. Also, when the patient's attention is distracted or you turn away, he may be able to move a paralyzed limb for a moment. This by no means should be mistaken for malingering, which is in a category of its own and is characterized by a planful, conscious, and quite persistent intention to deceive.

With respect to the differential diagnosis between conversion hysteria, malingering, and hypochondriasis, let us take the symptom of visual impairment as an example: where the hysterically "blind" person will somehow manage to avoid an obstacle in his path, the malingerer will bump into it—the difference being caused by the malingerer's concentrated intention to prove his illness to the examiner, whereas this intention is missing in the hysterical person. If you confront the hysterical patient with his lapse, he may be hurt or feel that you do not understand him, but usually he will not insist upon the seriousness of his disability as determinedly as will the malingerer if the latter's illness is questioned. The person with hypochondriasis, in turn, will receive the assurance that he is not organically ill with deep distrust and negative feelings, even with contempt for your ability as a doctor, because his complaints are based upon a type of psychopathology that leads to the rigid conviction of his serious physical disturbance. This is not the case with either the hysterical patient or the malingerer. Neither the malingerer nor the hypochondriacal patient seeks to establish a positive relationship with the physician in the way that is characteristic for the hysterical patient. The malingerer tries to conceal his intention of achieving a gain (financial compensation or evading responsibility) through establishing "organic" illness, and thus he perceives the doctor as a spy and as his antagonist. In many instances the malingerer shows psychopathic character traits and impulsive or antisocial behavior. The true or severe hypochondriac, who is usually a borderline personality or actually psychotic, sees the doctor not as someone who relieves him of anxiety, but as an incompetent or inconsiderate person who does not understand the serious danger in which the patient sees himself, and who does not truly want to help the patient. This type of psychological disturbance frequently is combined with paranoid personality trends so that the patient's medical environment becomes in his fantasies a group of enemies who want to make him suffer more. Such severe cases are relatively rare in most medical practice. However, there are found even in normal individuals transient hypochondriacal features, which include in a milder form similar tendencies to insist on a grave diagnosis and to doubt and question the competence of anyone who does not agree.

3. In the next group are hysterical symptoms which seem to present themselves as disturbances in the area of intellectual functioning. They appear as disorders of perception, memory, the state of consciousness, the patient's awareness of his personal identity, or his sensing and testing of reality. Again, as was the case in the two previous groups, there is no actual mental decompensation, in contrast to the psychoses. The diagnostic term for these symptoms is *dissociation hysteria*, but perhaps *hysterical ego dysfunction* is a more accurate comprehensive designation. The manifestations are often quite dramatic. Among them are amnesias and fugue states in which important data are forgotten, like the patient's own name and past history. He may leave the scene of a traumatic event and arrive somewhere else without knowing how or why he got there. It can be demonstrated that this is not a major organic deficit in memory—as you might find in a Korsakoff psychosis—because, in hypnosis, it is relatively easy to recover the forgotten events and the awareness of personal identity in hysterical amnesias and fugue states; the knowledge is there, but it is repressed.

The syndrome of multiple personality, of which a number of classical cases have been studied and reported, is a related, largely dissociative kind of reaction; in each personality state the individual is "unaware" of the other states and has a separate identity with different standards, preferences, moods, etc. Sleepwalking is a milder form of fugue. Hysterical "twilight states" of dramatic confusion resembling organic delirium are found in this group of disturbances; they frequently feature another hysterical personality disorder, namely, pseudologia phantastica or pathological lying. This occurs typically in adolescence and represents the acting out of a fantasy; what is real and what the patient would like to be the reality are for him so close together that he bring his fantasy to you as the truth. The teenage girl who describes vividly an imagined sexual attack, or the young man with the improbable success story may belong in this group. There is a gradual transition from ordinary wishful thinking to this symptom. In a special form of hysterical ego dysfunction called the Ganser syndrome, the patient gives the appearance of mental irresponsibility by making childish errors in familiar activities and by giving approximate and quite incorrect answers to simple questions. There is an anecdote which portrays this best: three drunks are riding on the subway. The first asks, "What time is it?" The second looks at his cigarette lighter and replies, "Thursday," whereupon the third announces, "Then we must get off." These answers and reactions are typical for the Ganser syndrome, provided that they are not produced by alcohol as in this story.

Having completed our description of hysteria as a neurosis, we find its behavioral manifestations in the attenuated form of the *hysterical personality*. In it we find character traits which reflect traces of the symptomatology we have just described. In order to present the personality type more succinctly, we shall somewhat accentuate the features; you will encounter their explicit and less highlighted manifestations in connection with problems of medical management frequently enough. From the picture of hysteria presented thus far, we are not surprised to find that this type of person impresses us as lively, has a wide range of strong affective reactions, and is prone to develop anxieties or physical complaints. This is the person who may scream because of a slight, sudden noise, or feel almost paralyzed or faint in a stressful situation. Emotions influence the person's thinking intensely. Whatever arouses a powerful positive or negative affective reaction will tend to carry the weight of a conviction. Consistency, accuracy, or reliability are not these persons' greatest strengths. They have considerable difficulty in knowing, or being able to recall, what they do not want to know. They may fluctuate in their enthusiasms, becoming equally excited in turn about opposing points of view. Such a person may have a vivid imagination and an artistic bent, may live in the moment, and dramatize all experiences. According to prevailing emotions, he or she is overenthusiastic, hilarious, moody, or tearful.

Especially characteristic is a diffuse erotization of experiences and of personal relationships, which are usually varied and numerous. The woman with the hysterical personality often is coy, coquettish, and seductive, but becomes upset, even horrified, if this leads to a direct amorous advance toward her. In the sexual act she tends to be inhibited or frigid. The hysterical man is equally a charmer. He displays his virility and competitive powers as a man, and yet has the aforementioned readiness for anxiety and, more specifically, is apprehensive and prone to inhibitions with regard to active sexual mastery and potency.

Hysterical personalities are preoccupied in their fantasy life with romantic, idealized, erotic imagery of the unsophisticated, adolescent variety that is found in the "true-to-life" kind of magazine story or the routine movie plot. Straight sex is banished from these daydreams or belongs only to the villain, while the hero is masterful and gentle, protecting the honor of women in distress, and the heroine remains pure and swoons. A forbidden, unconscious fantasy of the abducting caveman will be transformed in this way into something genteel and sublime.

In marriage, when sex enters the picture, the hysterical woman may consider her husband a "brute"; and correspondingly, the hysterical man yearns for a more elevated, "pure" wife. Such fantasies, which were widespread in the Victorian era and conformed to its ideal, are less frequent today and are likely to be found in artless, strictly brought-up adolescents, often from old-fashioned or isolated families with rigid moral codes.

To find a unifying concept underlying this multiplicity of symptoms and traits comprising hysterical reactions, let us turn to the illness of Jennifer, a sixteen-year-old, agoraphobic girl, which has been studied in detail in an extensive psychoanalysis. It shows little of the complicated and confusing elaboration of the neurotic system that usually occurs in the case of an older person with a neurosis of long standing. And it clearly demonstrates the close connection between fantasies and symptoms.[1] Jennifer's neurosis, when fully established, consisted in an extensive phobic system, the center of which was a fear of leaving her home, combined with an intense fear of heights. She was afraid of traveling, of bridges and of elevators, and while at home had to be as close to the earth as possible, if necessary on the ground floor holding onto the rug. This culminated in a very unusual fear that gravity would cease and everything would fly off into space, so that she might lose contact with her home and with the earth. There was the dread of the infinite, of open spaces, and the starry firmament. In addition, she suffered from fears of matches, of fire, of the heat of the summer, and of the color red. A special feature of her problem was the panic at the thought of passing through a square frequented by young men and women students.

The main elements in the history of this girl, particularly her relationship to her father and mother, show the influence of the basic oedipus complex. Practically from birth her relationship to her mother was a tense, conflicting one; there were severe feeding difficulties, which had begun with pylorospasm, requiring medical intervention, in the newborn child. The mother was very dedicated to her daughter, but at the same time overinvolved in the conflict around eating, which had continued throughout the years. She even went so far as

[1] The recognition of the role of fantasy in symptom formation was one of the most dramatic episodes and marked an important turning point in Freud's early research. Until then, in view of the material reported by his patients, he felt forced to believe that the pathogenic core of hysteria and obsessional neurosis was the experience of sexual seduction in childhood. But in his further work, in 1897, he found reason to invalidate this conclusion and gained the insight that in most cases this material was related to a fantasy and not a real experience. He recognized that the fantasies to which psychoneurotic patients traced back their symptoms may have pathogenic significance equal to that of real events (Freud, 1897).

to distribute food in the house, inconspicuously, with the hope that Jennifer, if not requested directly, might eat some of this food. The youngster, who understood her mother's intentions very well, carefully avoided doing so. Her main food intake was done at night by icebox raiding. All of this reflected the daughter-mother conflict as we so often see it in its extreme form in the behavior of the adolescent.

The girl's relationship to her father was a very close, admiring one, and he returned the child's affection generously in a very outspoken way, in contrast to the mother, who was a rather reserved woman. Although the mother was not aggressive, she adhered strictly to moral standards in keeping with her own rigid upbringing and her social position; it was difficult for her to make allowances or to indulge in an easy-going attitude. In past years the mother had repeatedly left town to visit her own mother who was chronically ill, so that there were frequent periods when the little girl and the father stayed home together, which created a kind of special friendship between them.

Jennifer had to be treated at her home for a long time because of the insurmountable difficulty she had in leaving the house and going away from where she felt protected. She could leave the house only with great effort and only if her mother accompanied her. We shall now discuss mainly those parts of the case material which specifically refer to our topic and which will help us to understand the working of the hysterical mechanisms leading to this severe neurosis.

The most characteristic and outstanding activities of this patient when she was younger were a series of regular and copious daydreams, each of which she pursued for a long time, sometimes for over a year, repeating the same type of images until she replaced them by another set of fantasies. At the age of six or seven she daydreamed for hours while swaying to and fro on a swing in their backyard. The earliest version of her daydreams consisted of a little story in which she owned a house in the woods all by herself. She fixed up this house according to her own taste. She did not have to ask anyone what she might do. Nobody was around and nobody gave her advice. The second set of daydreams, which appeared approximately two years later, involved her dreams of traveling. They usually started out in the following way: mother was going to visit grandmother and the little girl and father went on a trip. Later on she frequently omitted this explanatory introduction and either started out alone on the trip or, if she went together with her father, he soon was left behind. She traveled as far east or south as her imagination permitted, all by herself, but she always met a small expedition under the leadership of an elderly, elegant, slim, gray-templed explorer, who took her on as his little assistant. The daydream usually ended with her being crowned princess and ruler of the country where they met, be it India, China, or an imaginary state far away from home. A third and latest set of daydreams pertained to the dreams about Starman: during dinner sitting with her parents and frequently not eating but just pushing her food around on the plate, she impatiently awaited the end of the meal with the fantasy that the Starman was standing outside at the corner expecting her to meet him. After the meal, continued her daydreams, she imagined leaving the house, taking the Starman by the hand, and flying off with him into space, into the infinite, to the moon and stars.

Around the age of thirteen, in puberty, Jennifer developed an intense crush on a boy who was president of the senior class in high school. It was interesting to hear from the patient that she never spoke to this boy. She had only looked at him longingly from afar in school and he probably never knew about her feelings for him. Her neurosis had its onset immediately after a dream about him. The dream was as follows: she was mountain climbing with him and as they reached the top she suddenly felt the ground crumbling under her feet. She tried to hold onto the ledge which gave way, and in an extreme panic, struggling for a firm hold in order not to fall down the mountain, she failed and woke up in terror. After this fearful nightmare, her phobic restrictions developed in short succession, and within a few weeks she could not go to school any more and developed one symptom after the other. She could not leave the house, she could not travel, she could not go over bridges, and so forth, as was pointed out at the beginning of this history.

We can show in this case, though rarely in such pure form, almost all of the phobic symptoms first appearing in the preadolescent, pleasurable daydreams; the fantasy of being a homemaker in her own right, setting up her house without any interference from mother, and of going off with her father, who later turned into the elderly explorer, and becoming the first lady of the land, represented the dangerous and forbidden thoughts underlying her phobias of leaving the house, leaving mother, or going on a trip. Her habit of pursuing these daydreams while swinging for hours in the backyard entered into another group of phobias. The physical sensation of this activity, which had a masturbatory character, combined with the charged daydreams, found later expression in her inability to use elevators and her fears of heights and bridges.

The dream in which she climbed the mountain with the boy whom she loved is the connecting link in our understanding of this special set of phobias. These sensations on the swing, in elevators, and in high places were associated with physical, sexual feelings and symbolized for the girl sexual excitement. As such, they belonged to the most forbidden sensations after the outbreak of her neurosis. The symbolic meaning of her flying off into space with the Starman belonged in this group of reactions and showed the transformation of an intense wish into a terrifying anxiety. The phobic counterpart of this sensation was her fear that gravity might stop and that she would fall off into the infinite.

In contrast to the first daydream where the little girl was asserting herself as the woman of the house, but where as yet no man appeared explicitly in the picture, we see a father figure as the additional important element in all of the later dreams, either acknowledged directly as her father or replaced by the "elderly explorer" or the Starman. In the nightmare where the boy who was the first real object of her adolescent erotic fantasies was introduced in a mountain-climbing episode, we see the switch from earlier, disguised daydreams to the fear of materializing these unconscious fantasies, leading to the panic and the subsequent phobic restrictions.

The square where the young girl students meet the boys became particularly frightening as representing so flagrantly the elements of her fantasies which seemed so threatening. Red and heat were symbols for passion and sex, and in discussing why she dreaded heat in the summer she used an interesting picture to explain her feelings. She felt that when it was hot the sun was too close to the earth and this closeness made her anxious. Because of her fear of red, which stood for "intense feelings" or passion, she surrounded herself protectively with pastel shades, particularly baby colors of pink and light blue.

With added appreciation of the function of fantasy in hysteria, both as a substitute for the satisfaction of unrealizable wishes and as an unconscious representation of instinctual tendencies, let us now try to summarize the theory of hysteria. An essential, predisposing factor is the original repression of sexual impulses and wishes which can be traced back to an unsuccessful attempt to solve the oedipus complex in childhood. This leads to the inhibition of normal sexual activities and discharge of sexual tensions. The inception of adult sexual reactions with the physiological changes of puberty and adolescence brings these conflicts to a head. As the instinctual pressure, which is recurrently built up in an active biological process, is constantly held back from discharge by unconscious restrictions, the theory assumes that this sexual tension builds up, leading to a general state of erotic excitation or excitability and to a series of more or less disguised erotic fantasies. If additional, precipitating experiences of an intensifying nature occur, as, for example, marriage, or even the first date, these erotic fantasies or erotic physical sensations may become the center of symptoms.

We are familiar with the normal, consciously perceived heightening of physical erotic tension that occurs as part of sexual forepleasure; at such times touches and odors, sights and sounds have increased power to excite pleasure. These physical reactions involve the central nervous system, as well as endocrine and other chemical processes. The very same pathways seem to be involved in the physical manifestations of conversion hysteria, based upon unconscious erotic fantasies. The linking up of ordinarily neutral ideas with sexual fantasies, and the influence of these fantasies upon emotions, thinking, body functions, and behavior, underlies hysterical conversion symptoms, phobias, ego dysfunctions, and personality reactions.

Hysteria by no means comprises all of the problematic or adaptive consequences that may result from the early sexual conflicts, but the mechanisms which we have so far discussed take a central position in the outcome of these childhood problems and permit us to consider some of their implications for medical management.

It is well known that attention by the physician to psychological processes is indicated and frequently important from the very beginning of his contact with his patients. In the case of a young hysterical girl, Margaret, who showed many typical personality features, the influence of her fantasy life was already apparent during the diagnostic evaluation. The house physician in charge of the Emergency Ward asked the psychiatrist to see this sixteen-year-old girl, who had painful paresthesias in the small of her back and had developed a sudden paralysis of both legs. Poliomyelitis was prevalent at the time and the possibility of organic disease was being seriously investigated. Nevertheless, in the course of the examination, as the physician noted the patient's emotional state, her coy, almost flirtatious behavior and her shifting statements about the nature of her complaints following his examination, he thought that there might be a marked hysterical element present.

When the psychiatrist arrived at the Emergency Ward, he found one of the doctors, both concerned and embarrassed, sitting on the bed, the patient pinning him down, so to speak, in a perfect hysterical arch. This is a kind of fit where the patient lies in a tonic muscular spasm, resting only on her shoulders and heels in a rigid and sometimes slightly convulsive state. In the case of our patient the doctor, who was considering the possible diagnosis of hysteria, had wanted to be doubly sure that no organic condition would be overlooked. So, in the course of his systematic neurological examination, he had the patient sit up with the help of a nurse while he sat behind her on the side of the bed, cautiously examining her back by softly pounding her vertebrae; this had suddenly precipitated the hysterical seizure.

In two brief interviews with the patient it was learned that Margaret was quite a romantic little girl, very frightened by real life, who had grown up in a sheltered, somewhat inhibited family with a strict, religious tradition. Emphasis had always been placed upon the sinfulness of sexuality. In order to escape from the wicked things of the world she had prepared herself inwardly for a clean, safe existence, wanting to enter a convent in preparation for going to the far East as a missionary (this plan seemed to be an unconscious compromise between self-denial and seeking adventure). In spite of these resolutions she had given in to the persuasion of her friends and had gone with them to her first dance. She had danced a great deal, always with the same, very handsome boy from the neighborhood, and this had clearly excited her and stimulated her fantasies. Then she had left with her girlfriends, and in the subway she suddenly collapsed with a terrible pressure in the small of her back, "like a plate of lead."

It turned out that this was the place where her partner had held his hand as they danced. Finally, these very same fantasies and the ensuing anxiety over them were provoked and intensified during the physical examination, particularly when this place on her back was touched.

The internist's understanding of the patient's hysterical behavior led to the appropriate diagnosis. However, a knowledge of personality features, though they are not always as well defined as in this case, is not only important for the correct diagnosis, but helps us formulate some guiding principles in the management of patients having similar characteristics. Such cases are quite frequently encountered in medical practice. The relatively normal, well-adjusted adult of this type will usually make a warm, lively, and colorful impression. He resembles in a moderate degree the picture we find in more pathological form in the hysterical patient. Strong affective reactions, suggestibility, the tendency to deny anxiety-laden experiences, and dramatization in speech, dress, and behavior accompany the inclination to eroticized, highly idealized relationships. Both men and women with this personality makeup want to be noticed and admired as attractive and outstanding. In the medical setting the hysterical kind of woman consciously or unconsciously seeks the male doctor's appreciation. She may bring out, in an inviting way, her defenselessness and need for gallant support and protection. During illness this sometimes takes the form of a display of suffering. Her relationship to women in this environment is more neutral or even negative. The idealized or more directly sensual fantasies of the hysterical man are directed toward nurses, social workers, and women physicians while male doctors are seen as powerful authorities and rivals. Such a patient may repeatedly demonstrate, attempt to prove, and exaggerate his manliness, strength, and courage. At the same time he may show a surprising degree of anxiety when he must undergo a minor surgical procedure or other experiences having the unconscious meaning of severe mutilation and, in the final analysis, castration.

The overriding significance of these unconscious elements, as compared with sometimes even the most ominous reality problems, could be observed in the case of Mr. K., a thirty-eight-year-old man who suffered from carcinoma of the rectum. This strong, overbearing, and rather bossy navy yard laborer faced the serious operation and the poor prognosis of his condition with unusual courage. He was well liked by other patients and was playfully attentive to the nurses and other women personnel on the ward. This relative equanimity suddenly changed after what seemed to the environment to be a minor medical event: during the period of convalescence in the hospital he had to undergo the extraction of two teeth. He became agitated and threatened suicide. At the same time his behavior toward his social worker became frankly seductive: he made passes at her and clearly indicated his strong masculine desires. He showed us the role which his beautiful teeth had played in his life: they had always been his and his mother's special pride. To lose them profoundly threatened his self-image of an attractive male. This represented for him a most tragic loss and, in order to deny it, he felt compelled to play a seductive role with the social worker. In contrast, his carcinoma did not have the same significance with regard to his concept of masculinity, and thus he could cope far better with the much more serious operation. However, there was one thing that troubled him in his adjustment to his major illness, and this was in keeping with his reaction to the removal of his teeth. When he learned that because of a postoperative urinary fistula it was necessary for him to squat down in order to urinate, he became very fearful of being discovered in such a feminine position by the other men at his place of work.

The anticipation and experience of surgery frequently arouse anxiety based upon the intensely charged fantasies associated with the conflicts of the oedipal phase. In a study of the reactions of children to tonsillectomy it was found that the anxiety of older children was focused around anesthesia and the operation itself. This was related to unconscious fears of punishment for sexual fantasies which led to anxieties about bodily damage or even death. The younger children who had not yet reached this stage of development became anxious largely because of their separation from their parents during hospitalization (Jessner and Kaplan, 1949).

The problem of preparation for surgery was highlighted in the case of two brothers, Larry and Kenny, close to each other in age, who entered our hospital at the same time. When tonsillectomy was advised for both of them, Kenny, a rather tense youngster with a number of anxieties, developed marked fears. In this context Kenny gave his parents and others in his environment much difficulty, but also the opportunity to talk about the operation, to reassure him, and explain the process to him. In this way they helped him in handling the anxiety and in bringing it down from extreme fantasy to an unpleasant but basically not too threatening reality. Larry, on the other hand, was characterized by a certain indifference, or at least what seemed an indifference toward physical dangers. He was rather courageous and unconcerned, and had neither requested nor participated in any special discussion of the oncoming operation. The disparity between these two youngsters was still quite marked in the way they went up to the operating room, Kenny just about to cry, Larry laughing and perhaps showing for the first time signs of overconfidence. The surgeon reacted accordingly with great approval of the courageous one and with some intolerance toward the upset boy.

Immediately after the operation the picture was very different. Kenny, relieved of his major tension, was comfortable in spite of pain and was emphasizing, as one hears so often in these overanxious patients, how much less terrible it had been than he had expected. Larry, lying in the next bed, was in an absolute turmoil, screaming as if his confident and secure world had broken down, and it took a great deal of effort to reassure and comfort him.

Kenny's successful preparation for surgery illustrates certain general principles that apply in the medical management of the hysterical personality. Within the limits permitted by his concerned, but not excessively solicitious environment, he was able to give verbal and affective expression to his fears, reminding us of Breuer and Freud's discovery of the importance of emotional abreaction in alleviating neurotic manifestations. In addition to the opportunity to express pent-up feelings in an acceptable form, the hysterical patient benefits from assistance in separating his alarming fantasies from reality. As in the case of this boy, a calm, clear, though not necessarily elaborate or systematic, discussion of medical procedures will often help. With a tense, suggestible person, the physician will do well not to show too great concern about symptoms, beyond what is involved in carefully searching for the diagnosis and in thorough medical treatment and follow-up.

The hysterical kind of patient seeks a reciprocal warmth and wants to be appreciated as an interesting and lively person; for this reason it would be an error for the doctor to be cold and aloof. At the same time, in view of the hysterical person's readiness for erotically colored fantasies, the doctor will have to remain aware of the possibility that his actions and expressions may take on a special meaning for such a patient. Therefore, a certain reserve and the avoidance of too intense, too personal an approach on the part of the physician might best accompany his friendly and interested attitude.

Furthermore, the better the physician understands certain psychological elements related to the illness, the more successful he can be in his medical management. For a man of the hysterical personality type, illness represents specifically a threat to strength and achievement. It helps such a person if the doctor provides some support and reassurance, e.g., by acknowledging the interest the patient evokes in people and the strong and attractive impression he makes upon his environment. Similarly, illness may provoke fear of loss of attractiveness to the hysterical woman, and thus call for appropriate attention to relieve this anxiety. For men and women infirmity may represent the retaliation for early oedipal wishes. All this can be understood better if the physician pays close attention to the patient's characteristic reactions to illnesses in the past, to repetitive patterns in the patient's personal relationships brought about by sickness or by therapeutic procedures, and to whatever the case history reveals of the patient's early emotional experiences.

7

Early School Years: The Latency Period

The child's effort to solve the oedipus complex, leading to the establishment of the superego, ushers in a new phase of great inner development and adjustment, during which the main features of his future adult personality are established. From about five or six years of age on, intellectual growth and sophistication are in the foreground. The age of school learning extends at least into early adolescence, to about age fourteen, in all countries that have the economic means for basic education. We call the years from approximately six to twelve the period of sexual latency because, after his first five to six years when the child has psychologically established his infantile instinctual patterns, the latter remain rather stable until the changes of puberty set in. As seen in our culture, masturbation and sexual curiosity diminish or temporarily appear to cease, while subtler and more sublimated expressions of affection and the urge for achievement based upon the appreciation of being part of the family group largely replace the earlier childhood sexual and aggressive strivings.

In this time of relative rest from instinctual pressures the child forms his work habits and his attitudes toward his intellectual life. He sets up the standards for his inner laws as

121

to what he can permit himself and what he has to prohibit. He builds up his ways of transforming primitive emotions and drives, through sublimation and reaction formation, into socially acceptable responses: an oral tendency to take in everything greedily may become an intellectual hunger with widespread interests or studiousness; stubbornness can change into energetic tenacity, and aggressiveness into active leadership and protective strength; anxious passivity and dependence may become changed into cooperative, helpful, and unselfish attitudes, and hypersensitivity into an intense interest in justice. The process of consolidating the superego is well represented in the children's games of this period; they center around the struggle between good and evil, between cops and robbers, cowboys and Indians, etc. During this metamorphosis, especially in its early phases, the child sometimes shows the uneven combination of strict, serious grown-up qualities and of babyishness.

Latency is a time of forming new relationships. Feelings hitherto concentrated upon the parents and siblings may now be displaced to a larger number of teachers and classmates. The child may love some of these substitute figures and hate others. He has the opportunity to choose friends who can supply or make up for what he may lack or must contend with at home. These favored playmates, in contrast to his siblings, can be selected by him and will be stronger or weaker according to his own needs. He moves steadily toward greater independence as his world broadens, and he adds to his early figures of identification new models from among his teachers, schoolmates, and newly discovered characters from fiction, historical personalities, and popular heroes.

Some antagonism toward his parents may be expressed at home during the latency period, but it is often compensated in the exaggerated, even boastfully positive stories of the exploits of family members that are told to other children or adults. A close friendship formed with another child of the same sex and age, in which activities and small adventures are undertaken together, tends to reassure and strengthen the latency youngster in his quest for greater self-reliance. Knowledge of all sorts is shared in this alliance, particularly concerning information or misinformation about sexual and reproductive functions. It is discussed intently, away from the intrusive authority of the adult world. In general the boys play almost exclusively with other boys, and the girls stay with girls. A boy who spends too much time with the girls runs the risk of being considered a sissy. The girls, in turn, may feel indifferent toward the boys and consider them wild and stupid.

This is the general outline of development at this time for the boy and girl who have accepted their psychological and biological sexual differences. Within this framework one sees various special constellations indicating some unsolved underlying conflicts. For example, tomboyishness, including playing with the boys exclusively as one of them, is a frequent, transitory development for many girls in this phase, representing a residue of the envy of the boy's body and role. Similarly, there are boys who avoid sports or prefer noncompetitive or peaceful activities with girls, as an expression of their persisting insecurity and anxiety.

As the child begins to compare his father and mother with other grownups in a more realistic way, and no longer sees his parents as extremely unique and ideal figures, and as he slowly moves away from intense and intimate closeness to them, he will frequently have daydreams of a characteristic, compensatory form—"family romances" in which the parents are replaced by others of more exalted social position. The fantasy that "I am really a prince, secretly given to this humble family for safe keeping at birth" can permit the youngster to sidestep or displace certain problems: the taboos attached to one's "ordinary" mother and father are set aside; forbidden closeness and rivalry may be displaced to the royal parents; one gets rid of the siblings, etc.

Even though many adults do not consciously remember

having had such fantasies, we can find them undisguised in the books which have the greatest appeal to youngsters in latency and early puberty. With an abundance of everyday detail and almost monotonous regularity, the tales that are so eagerly read at this time repeat certain themes: the child hero of the story suddenly moves from lowly poverty to a palace, or vice versa; he or she is very moral and brave, and often succeeds in overcoming, taming, and sometimes redeeming an irascible or wicked grownup; the child is an orphan or only one parent is living, usually the parent of the opposite sex. The youngster's progress in reading from *Heidi*, *Treasure Island*, and *Robinson Crusoe*, to *Jane Eyre* and *David Copperfield* will presage the reawakening of the sexual life at puberty (Friedlander, 1942).

For many children striving to establish self-control in this phase, occasional episodes of anxiety at night, of bed wetting or temper tantrums, may represent a necessary breakthrough of tension. When more definite disturbances in personality development occur, they frequently take the form of difficulty in adjusting to social demands, or represent problems created by establishing too rigid inner controls. A child might have difficulties in school, a very common complaint during these years, on the basis of either of these reactions. On the one hand, a continuation of childhood attitudes, such as egocentric tendencies and a dislike of any strain that is imposed, could interfere with sublimation and lead to a block in learning; fear or reluctance to loosen the parental ties is frequently a factor in the phobia of going to school; defiance of authority, aggressive behavior, or disturbed relationships with other children can be the result of this lack of inner adjustment.

On the other hand, excessively strong restrictions and methods of defense against undesirable tendencies and forbidden fantasies may also lead to anxiety centering around school, or to failures in achievement and in personal relationships. In the most marked form of disturbance due to extreme restraint, explosively aggressive behavior now appears in children who up to this time have been excessively good, neat, obedient, and pliable, and this behavior may signal the beginning stage of obsessional neurosis, with its ritualistic symptoms in eating, washing, dressing, or going to bed. Some of these children may already have shown in early childhood forerunners of these obsessional behavior patterns. Another group among these self-controlling youngsters are the perfectionistic children. They do well during this phase and are praised for this by their parents and teachers, only to become bogged down in an inordinate preoccupation with small details and paralyzed by the tendency to doubt everything later on. While the child who is overly aggressive, defiant, fearful, shy, or failing in school will often be brought for professional advice and help, the overconscientious child is often overlooked if he does not accidentally come to the attention of a specially informed and perceptive observer.

As the latency period gradually comes to a close, its stability gives way to many shifts and changes during puberty, the first of the important critical periods that characterize adult existence. Crises as decisive, culminating moments in life are most familiar to the physician in the form of the changes in extremely acute and severe illnesses, which indicate the movement toward recovery or death. But in a broader sense crises occur normally as turning points in the life of the individual and lead to acute disequilibria, which under favorable conditions result in specific maturational steps toward new functions. Each of the principal developmental crises, whether of early childhood, puberty, pregnancy, menopause, or old age, has biological, psychological, and social aspects. An appreciation of these phases is of value for the physician's general understanding of adult personalities, and also because patients frequently turn to their doctors with symptoms of physical distress that are related to these upheavals.

SUGGESTED READING

INFANCY: THE CENTRAL NEEDS

Abraham, K. (1924), The Influence of Oral Erotism on Character Formation. *Selected Papers on Psychoanalysis*, 1:393-406.

Freud, S. (1905b), Three Essays on the Theory of Sexuality (*Standard Edition*, 7:123-243). These essays, which gave the psychoanalytic study of personality development its main impetus, provide an essential basis for the chapters on individual development. It may be helpful as preparation to read first Lectures XX and XXI of Freud's Introductory Lectures on Psycho-Analysis (1916-1917) (*Standard Edition*, 16:303-328).

Spitz, R. A. (1945, 1946), Hospitalism. *The Psychoanalytic Study of the Child*, 1:53-74; 2:113-117. One of the pioneering studies of the impact of extreme deprivation of mothering in infancy.

EARLY MASTERY OF BODY FUNCTIONS

Abraham, K. (1921), Contributions to the Theory of the Anal Character. *Selected Papers on Psychoanalysis*, 1:370-392.

Freud, S. (1908), Character and Anal Erotism (*Standard Edition*, 9:167-175).

SEXUAL DIFFERENTIATION: THE OEDIPUS COMPLEX AND ITS RESOLUTION

Abraham, K. (1925), Character Formation on the Genital Level of Libido Development. *Selected Papers on Psychoanalysis*, 1:407-417.

Deutsch, H. (1944-1945), *The Psychology of Women*, 2 Volumes (New York: Grune & Stratton). Details feminine psy-

126

chological development from infancy through old age, including pregnancy and motherhood.

Freud, S. (1924), The Dissolution of the Oedipus Complex (*Standard Edition*, 19:173-179).

Freud, S. (1933), New Introductory Lectures on Psycho-Analysis. Lecture XXXIII on "Femininity" (*Standard Edition*, 22:112-135).

SEXUAL DIFFERENTIATION: NEUROSIS, PERSONALITY, AND MEDICAL MANAGEMENT

Breuer, J. & Freud, S. (1893-1895), Studies on Hysteria (*Standard Edition*, Vol. 2).

Easser, B. R. & Lesser, S. R. (1965), Hysterical Personality: A Re-evaluation. *Psychoanalytic Quarterly*, 34:390-405.

Freud, S. (1905a), Fragment of an Analysis of a Case of Hysteria (*Standard Edition*, 7:3-122).

EARLY SCHOOL YEARS: THE LATENCY PERIOD

Lindemann, E. & Dawes, L. G. (1952), The Use of Psycho-analytic Constructs in Preventive Psychiatry. *The Psychoanalytic Study of the Child*, 7:429-448. The latency period is considered especially with a view to the opportunities it offers for the pre-vention of mental and emotional disturbance, by Lydia G. Dawes in the report of a community mental health project.

Bornstein, B. (1951), On Latency. *The Psychoanalytic Study of the Child*, 6:279-285. This article, in its depth, is extremely interesting to psychoanalysts and psychiatric instructors, but rep-resents advanced reading for students with special interest in child development and psychotherapy.

Part III

PUBERTY AND ADOLESCENCE

8

Puberty and Adolescence

Starting usually in prepuberty at about ten or twelve years of age, children enter the period of rapid physical development marked by skeletal growth, changes of body contour, and sexual maturation, which, as we know, is accelerated by approximately two years in girls. Puberty designates the attainment of sexual maturity. Adolescence refers to the entire period of somatic and psychological change beginning with puberty and extending to the establishment of psychological adulthood in the early twenties.

The changes in body structures and function at puberty are accompanied by an upsurge of instinctual pressure and a gradual psychological unsettling of the normally steady and relatively untroubled course of personality consolidation, intellectual achievement, and increasing ability to cope with and adapt to the world that has been typical of the latency period. The sexual drive is reawakened and greatly intensified, and this is preceded and accompanied by a revival of aggressive tendencies and urges that seek and embody early oral and anal satisfactions. With increasing intensity the whole repressed instinctual life of childhood, now supported by the physiologically reinforced drives, pounds against the walls of repression and restrictions; and this impact of drives and of their derivative emotions and fantasies is met by an equally strong attempt to re-establish or keep up the former peaceful and well-organized inner life of the latency period. The result is the picture that the youngster at puberty offers to his surprised and often distressed environment.

It shows the struggle between the two opposing tendencies, the instinctual breaking through and the defense of the ego leading to the most amazing contrasts seen sometimes in the same person, almost side by side.[1] Adolescents are markedly egocentric and nevertheless ready for sacrifice as perhaps never again in later life; they are full of passionate affection, and yet surprisingly aloof and inconsiderate; affected in manner, with a burning desire for sincerity; ascetic and indulgent in a most infantile form; shy and exhibitionistic; rude and sensitive; enthusiastically hard-working, and lazily dull; blindly submissive to their leaders, and equally blindly rebellious toward authorities; dirty and unkempt, but disgusted by vulgarity and coarseness; filled with longing for the group, and with a strong need for loneliness; swept by waves of optimism and deepest pessimism; strongly attached to their families, whom at the same time they fight in provocative ways.

While the adolescent's inner strife represents a revival of the infantile wishes and fantasies and of the old reactions against them in the form in which they had been left years ago, it is no longer a weak, childish play. It is now an encounter in earnest, with full force and great impact upon reality, and the outcome of it is binding for the rest of his life. The original objects of the young person's early strivings now become the first focus of his tension. At times he appears bent upon overthrowing his parents' authority, renouncing their standards and becoming as different from them as possible. The parents are drawn directly into trivial or serious

[1] Here we follow Anna Freud's summary (1936, 1958) of the typical changes, disturbances of the psychic equilibrium, and contradictions in the personality at puberty.

struggles over clothes, money, diets, chores, studies, curfew hours, college or a job, and the use of the family car. If they are religious, the adolescent may be antireligious; and if they are agnostic, he may become overdevout. This opposition may contribute to his fervent interest in ideas and movements, conservative or radical, in politics (the old guard and the young turks), and art (the abstract versus the concrete), whether he is drawn toward becoming a football player, a scientist, a beatnik, or an existentialist, or whether he turns to inner experience through the use of drugs or by participating in social action.

Even when early development has left an optimum residue of confident trust in the parents, the adolescent must once more contend with his unconscious, tabooed feelings of love for them (now greatly intensified), and his repudiated wishes for their care and protection. This struggle involves the effort to overthrow the idealized image and standards of the parental figures set up in childhood and accepted with devoted obedience. Thus he fights his parents as a way of fighting his childhood needs, and freeing himself to develop from a dependent child to the grown-up individual who finally can become a parent.

Excessively "good" behavior or remaining too closely bound to the parents during this period suggests avoidance of the challenge of puberty. The tumult associated with breaking the childhood attachments may herald a better, more realistic relationship with the parents in the future. In order to gain the necessary emotional distance from the family the young person turns more and more to friends of his own age, both individually and in groups, and to other adults whom he accepts as leaders, a step already begun during the latency period in grammar school.

The adolescent's relationships with his companions and heroes allow him to share values which support him in the effort to cope with the threat of inner needs, while the group affords a testing ground for action. It is noteworthy that the adolescent group in its most rigidly organized form, the gang, resembles a primitive society, providing a strict code of group loyalty and initiation rites. The goals of the group are important determinants of whether adolescent action will be socially constructive or delinquent (Aichhorn, 1925). From the preceding it becomes comprehensible that these goals, as important as they are for society, are not the most important reasons for the adolescent to seek this community. The core of his needs is the search for companionship and mutual support in this new phase, so different from childhood. This is why efforts to take the youth off street corners and to stop the formation of wild gangs can be so successful as long as the youngsters are not forced back into isolation within their family compounds, but rather are offered the same kind of group structure, though with different and more constructive aims.

In the more flexibly structured kinds of adolescent group associations, in contrast to those of the latency period, boys and girls meet together. They search for the solutions to their intensified needs for sexual fulfillment and closeness in kissing games, playful roughhousing, or ardent intellectual discussions, which prepare the way for romantic dating, and eventual courtship and marriage. It is particularly in relation to the group, and increasingly with reference to the opposite sex, that we can observe the typical, intensified concern of adolescents about how they perform, measure up, and look to others. You will recall the example of Eric (Lecture 5), the handsome seventeen-year-old who was troubled by the unreasonable conviction that his ears stuck out prominently in an ugly manner. His excessive reaction illustrates in a dramatic way the general adolescent preoccupation with appearance; it also provides a further illustration of how this concern may be linked up with the conflicts over sexual urges and masturbation which are now reawakened with even greater intensity.

Masturbation, more conscious and prominent in the boy, is for either sex charged with the repressed fantasies of the oedipus complex. These revived genital conflicts stand at the center of the adolescent crisis. The attempt to find new solutions may be observed in the close friendships of young people. In latency, friendships between youngsters of the same sex involve the sharing of adventures and confidences. At puberty they continue at first to serve the mutual strengthening of both partners, and are then broadened to worship for the same heroes. This in turn gives way to competitive heterosexual attachments, and then to more independent dating and courting. Both boys and girls may be active by temperament during the latency period. The boy, by and large, will continue and even intensify this driving tendency toward mastery of the environment after puberty. With her menarche the girl becomes relatively more passive and turned inward, preparing in her fantasies and attitudes for future motherhood. She is less aware than the boy of direct sexual feelings and more prone to romantic, idealized, and sublimated experiences of love.

The sharply fluctuating and inconsistent behavior of the adolescent, with its frequently extreme contrasts, often arouses alarm, especially as it is known that many emotional disorders become manifest during this period. But a pathological outcome is more likely to follow premature concentration in a particular area of conflict. Anna Freud has observed that this might take the form of too abrupt and complete a displacement of positive feelings from the parents to persons and groups outside of the home; a more serious problem is an extreme and unyielding opposition to the parents in which love, dependence, and respect are changed to persistent hostility, revolt, and contempt. Finally, the adolescent might handle his conflict over the relationship with his parents not by fighting them but by despising himself as an unsuccessful opponent; this then can lead to compensatory fantasies of grandiose accomplishments or to a self-depreciative preoccupation with his physical and intellectual performance and appearance. The final outcome in the most serious cases might even be a regression of psychotic proportions. Among those with borderline and psychotic reactions we find extreme negation of impulses through fanatical asceticism (in which all pleasurable feelings are fought, even to the denial of bodily needs for food, protection, and rest), with pronounced intellectualization, or the absolute refusal to make any compromises, far beyond the familiar tendency of young persons to stand up for moral and aesthetic principles.

In healthy development, the very close family ties are progressively loosened, and with it the intense love and competitive fear stemming from the oedipus complex recede. The adolescent begins a serious search for his place in the world and for his vocation. The knowledge and skills which he began to accumulate and develop as part of his growing adaptive strength in the latency period must now be further advanced and increasingly directed toward attainable functions or careers in society. This is a matter of lively concern to the young person.

Erik H. Erikson (1959) has emphasized that the usual period of delay in our culture of perhaps two to ten years between genital maturity and the age of responsible independence and marriage, while contributing to adolescent tension, also allows important changes to take place which facilitate the consolidation of personality and the working out of a positive relation to the social environment. It is a period of experimentation with different roles in which the young person tests himself and the environment with regard to "how far he can go" in many directions.

Erikson summarized the gains that are necessary for the achievement of adulthood, at the close of adolescence, as representing the establishment of a stable ego identity. This refers to the integration of past and recent identifications, including those which the adolescent formed with his peer groups, the reconstitution of his ideals and standards on a more mature basis, the securing of an assured sense of continuity by linking his previous life experiences with objectively

founded plans for the future, a realistic appraisal of his potentials, coming to terms with the community's recognition of
him, and an appreciation of himself as a person as well as an
acceptance of his now fully developed body.

Identity formation accompanies new experiences throughout life, but it is of critical importance at the end of adolescence. Erikson has termed the failure to surmount this crisis
a diffusion or dispersion of identity. It frequently takes the
form of an extreme difficulty in making the choice of friends,
of occupation, of mores, etc., and an inability to concentrate
upon important tasks or a self-destructive preoccupation with
one-sided activities, together with a sense of urgency and yet
a fear of any change or binding commitment.

In our necessary concern with conflicts and failures in
adolescence, as we are confronted with them and as a way to
the deeper understanding of the normal processes, we should
never lose sight of the emotional richness and intensity of
this time. A poet recalled this period of his life in the following
metaphor:

> . . . everyone knows how boundless adolescence is. How-
> ever many decades accrue to us afterwards, they are
> powerless to fill that hangar, into which they fly for
> memories, separately and in crowds, day and night, like
> . . . aeroplanes for petrol. In other words, these years in
> our life form a part which excels the whole . . . [Paster-
> nak, 1931].

As physicians our respect for the young person is helped
by our available personal recollections and observations of this
period and grows out of our understanding of the biological
and psychological forces that motivate adolescents. In our
awareness of the adolescent's powerful impetus toward maturity we will not talk down to him as an adult to a child. And
only if we understand the changeability of adolescent behavior, its inherent contradictions, and the existence of child-

like attitudes alongside of adult strivings, can we remain flexible in our approach, and represent standards or set limits when necessary, without expecting to be rewarded by the young person's unqualified appreciation of our efforts. Our comprehension of the adolescent's intensity of feelings, his urge to break the parental ties, and his frequent self-absorption and loneliness until new friendships and attachments are formed, can be conveyed to him so that he does not feel all alone in the world with his problems. And with our willingness to listen without prying, he may provide us with the information that can allow us to offer him reassurance and understanding with regard to his anxieties.

For instance, the adolescent's worries may be largely related to bodily changes. During the awkward stage of rapid, irregular growth he or she can be particularly concerned with questions of size, overweight or skinniness, asymmetry of the body, attractiveness (especially in the girls), strength (in the boys), and skin blemishes. The intense feelings of modesty and shame that may follow breast development, the appearance of body hair, menarche, or masturbation, call for special thoughtfulness on the doctor's part in history taking and in the carrying out of a routine physical examination. A defect, disability, or limitation that could present a threat to the adolescent's self-esteem will frequently be denied. The sleeplessness, hypochondriacal complaints, headaches, or learning difficulties so often reported may arise on the basis of masturbation anxieties, and are expressed by the young person with embarrassment and difficulty. In order to arrive at the informative data without increasing existing inhibitions, we have to exercise patience and tact, avoiding blunt questioning and providing throughout the interview a quiet atmosphere of reassurance. Yet in spite of our effort to support and help the adolescent, he may carry his struggle to become independent of his parents into the doctor's office or the hospital, as representative of the parental authority.

Michael S., a young man of seventeen, was brought to a ward of our hospital with acute arthritis. He immediately requested a bed in the corner, explaining cryptically that he did not wish to be overheard by the other patients in the event that he talked in his sleep, since he was involved in a secret mission. He had been taken off a sinking ship that was smuggling arms to another country and was concerned lest he give away the names of others involved in this operation. We were called to see him because of the difficulties which he presented on the ward. He yelled at the physical therapist, fought with the house officers, and threw the salads that were on his tray at mealtimes upon the floor.

In our interview with him we learned that he had earlier tried to enter the Coast Guard, in spite of being under age, because he wanted to do something of great importance for the country. His father had run a factory doing essential government work, but the boy did not feel that helping his father was enough of a challenge. At the age of twelve, already a large boy, he would visit his father's plant and get into heated arguments with customers who would ask for Mr. S. (the father), whereupon Michael would insist that *he* was Mr. S. and could deal adequately with their requests.

He had been a very good student, but he left high school one day, never to return, after complaining about a headache, because his teacher doubted the seriousness of this condition. He explained his angry rejection of the salads by saying that they are sissy foods; he wanted a decent meal with a piece of meat. He was deeply troubled with the thought that his buddies might say that he had sneaked out on them, and if they came to the hospital to visit him they could think (like his high school teacher) that he was not really ill at all.

This boy's chief concern was "not to be a coward, but to be a man." The aggressive manner in which he threw his weight around was tied up with his being only seventeen years old and, indeed, unconsciously behaving as if he were much younger in his reaction to being ill.

We suggested that the physicians, nurses, and dieticians should avoid being placed in the position of "the grownups who didn't take me seriously" and, therefore, had to be fought, overcome, and devaluated by him. The medical personnel should acknowledge and take into account the patient's urgent desire to be a man—not a child. This might be accomplished best by stepping back from any direct conflict and indicating to the patient that keeping bed rest and accepting the help of the woman physiotherapist were actually signs of self-control and strength of will rather than passivity and childish self-indulgence. The patient was to be given a choice in the matter of diet and encouraged to work out the most suitable form of physical therapy through discussion with the physicians and the therapist. When these suggestions were followed, Michael's behavior changed markedly and the medical program could be carried through without difficulty.

There are contrasting circumstances in which the physician may become the temporary beneficiary of the adolescent's need to separate himself emotionally from his parents, shifting his allegiance to the doctor and identifying with him, which ensures excellent cooperation in medical procedures.

The tendency of young people to turn to older friends who can serve as new models for identification, away from the family circle, permitted us to help a sixteen-year-old boy who showed strong denial of a very serious, anxiety-provoking illness. Neil, a high school football hero, had injured his foot against a stone. The wound never healed properly. Both the patient and his parents stood by for almost a year without asking for systematic medical help in spite of the fact that his condition had worsened to the point where he could not attend school for several months. It became clear that the parents, who were not negligent in the usual sense and were of adequate intelligence, could not tolerate the possibility that there was something more seriously wrong with their only son. When he was finally brought to the hospital, a biopsy was performed and the diagnosis of sarcoma was established. Amputation was advised.

When Neil was told of the decision by the house physician, his unemotional, seemingly disinterested reply was: "All right, if you think it is necessary." On the following morning the night nurse reported that the boy had not slept at all and had complained that it was too warm in his room. He had told her that he did not like his doctor (who had informed him of the necessary operation) because he thought that the doctor was unfriendly. Further discussion of the surgery disclosed that the boy regarded the biopsy as the definitive procedure and insisted that the doctor had said that the amputation did not have to be done at this time.

In view of the patient's marked lack of appropriate reactions to the proposed operation—his sleeplessness which indicated underlying tension, as well as the change in his formerly trustful and well-disposed attitude toward his house physician, the persistent denial of the seriousness of his condition, and the distortion of what had been advised—we were seriously concerned that the operation could be followed by a severe emotional disturbance of psychotic proportions. Therefore, amputation was postponed for a week to allow emergency psychotherapy aimed at prevention of a mental breakdown.

The most prominent anxiety of the patient and his parents, underlying their denial that his injury had to be taken seriously, was the fear that he would have to give up his prominent position as the athletic leader of his group. For the patient this role embodied his ideal of masculinity. On the basis of this information we asked the Veterans Administration Hospital if they could help us find a young, sensible, and mature amputee veteran who would assist us in the psychotherapy of this boy. A much decorated war hero arrived who had lost both legs in combat. We shared with this man all that concerned us about the patient's emotional problems, what his reactions indicated to us, and the approach that might be helpful for the boy. We hoped that Neil would become better able to face his own tragedy by talking to a man who had mastered a similar personal disaster, even emerging as a hero, and who had the self-confidence to marry and have children.

To help Neil, this man was advised how to bring out the anxieties involved in such a situation. He showed the boy the way that he felt about his own life and talked with him about his own experiences, how he reacted to his injuries at first with despair, depression, and hatred. He spoke of the anxieties aroused by the prospect of going home and facing his family, friends, and his girl. His approach was a positive one, namely: "Life is much more difficult for you and me than for someone who has both legs . . . but we are men and we can do it."

The youthful football hero understood and accepted this man as his model of masculine strength. It was true that he developed intense anxiety as the day of the operation approached and he reacted to the amputation with grief and some depression, yet these feelings were now accessible to him and he could deal with them in a realistic and appropriate way. Finally, with continued psychotherapy through the period of rehabilitation, Neil became adjusted and reinstated in his group, not as a football player but as a fully accepted and highly admired member.

Not infrequently the physician will be consulted by an adult suffering from symptoms of tension that have arisen in response to the behavior of an adolescent son or daughter. Such a family disturbance sometimes results from the encounter between two individuals in crisis, an adolescent facing a parent who himself faces the problem of aging. Even a relatively stable parent may be put to a severe test by his adolescent child. The parent may find it difficult to allow the adolescent to become independent by degrees, may not be flexible enough to tolerate the temporary upsurges of childish behavior in the young person, may lose his perspective with regard to adolescent defiance, or may be uncertain and therefore inconsistent with regard to what to permit and where to draw the line.

The physician can make use of his understanding of the parent's personality structure as well as of his knowledge of adolescence in his endeavor to remedy such a situation. As an example we may consider the case of Mrs. L., a woman who had begun to suffer from headaches without any organic cause. In telling her history to the physician she soon spoke of a concurrent conflict and struggle with her adolescent daughter. The girl, well brought up and previously obedient, had started to keep irregular hours and seemed to the mother to be irresponsible in a number of ways. Mrs. L. worried about her daughter, stayed up late to await her return, but could not make any headway with her child. However, the physician was not convinced that the daughter's rebellious behavior exceeded the limits of a somewhat rebellious but normal adolescent reaction. The mother herself reported in the interview a variety of obsessive-compulsive concerns, which showed in the relentless and systematic way in which she pursued her housework, in the exactness with which she kept up her daily schedule, her overdevotion to cleanliness, including her preoccupation with digestive functions and their regulation.

A number of possible approaches to this problem suggest themselves. Can one support a woman in this difficulty by indicating to her that she should try to see the beauty of this period of adolescent development? Will it help to encourage her to share in the interests of her daughter, who takes pleasure in trying out more grown-up activities? Our acquaintance with the compulsive personality tells us that this formulation (which could allay the rivalry and guilt of a hysterical type of mother) is not a good approach. Instead, Mrs. L. was advised and assisted to understand better the adolescent and the struggle he goes through in becoming independent, which frequently leads to his somewhat excessive behavior. She was specifically made aware of the task of becoming an effective mother for an adolescent girl, which had to be different from her approach when she cared for her daughter as a small child.

In other words, she was reached through the emphasis upon those psychological mechanisms which she used best according to her personality structure. This means introducing the method of intellectual mastery by giving her more information and by appealing to her reason as well as to her high standards of duty.

We can easily perceive the difference in approach to a compulsive personality in contrast to a dependent, infantile mother. In the latter case, this way of proceeding would only increase her tension and anxiety, and would intensify the need for your continued and increasing involvement and support; whereas the compulsive mother finds some fulfillment and satisfaction in carrying out such a new assignment. She constantly makes strict demands upon herself, trying her strength in order to prove her discipline and self-control.

The parent's own personality, as in this example, is one factor that determines which aspects of adolescence prove most troublesome to the family in the individual case. We have indicated many of the general sources of parental concern, including the confusing contradictions in adolescent behavior, the rebelliousness and lack of consideration, the ideological and religious warfare, the infantile indulgence and carelessness combined with criticism that concentrates upon every discernible peculiarity of the parents, the preference for "bad" friends, and the like.

To these we must add the sexual development of young people as a very common worry to most parents. While the enlightened modern parent may try not to be troubled about masturbation and the dangers of promiscuity, he is often deeply concerned about the successful development of his adolescent children into mature men and women, their timidity or prematurity in dating and partying, and their competence to choose their future marital partners in keeping with the family tradition. As threatening as these problems often seem to the overanxious parent, they usually recede and after this period of inner turmoil the adolescent normally begins to find adequate solutions to permit adaptation and growth into adult life and maturity.

However, the outcome is not always as happy. Physicians know that serious mental illnesses have their onset during this period, especially in young patients who all through their childhood showed signs of difficulty in adjusting to the usual demands which the family and the environment make on the growing child. Among these disturbances, which include many kinds of psychopathology, we would like to draw attention to a group of patients who often present a diagnostic problem because the picture they offer in adolescence resembles an extreme form of adolescent crisis, featuring nonconformity, egocentricity, shyness, and the need for solitude. In these cases the crisis manifestations do not recede as they do in the healthy young person, and these individuals retain some characteristic peculiarities which we call the *schizoid personality*. We refer to the kind of patient who seems reserved, remote, even aloof, and uninvolved in everyday matters.

This person frequently attracts our attention because of his eccentric unconcern with conventional appearance, conduct, and style of existence, or an odd preoccupation with ideologies (usually of an idiosyncratic kind), unorthodox movements, and dietary and health fads. He may lack planfulness in organizing his life and may recognize only his own virtues and values. All of this is based upon a process of isolating himself and living, to a certain extent, in a world of his own. He is not inclined to share his feelings, interests, and goals with other people, nor may he be capable of doing so. His personal relationships are few and devoid of normal intensity, vitality, and commitment. This wall which he erects between his inner life and the outside world can result in his passing for a long time quite unnoticed or he may be regarded with mild approval because he makes few requests and seems independent.

Frequently this holds true in the hospital environment where this patient seems to blend into the background, in contrast to others who talk about their needs and complain about their symptoms. Mr. O., a man in his early thirties, was this type of patient. Admitted with a digestive ailment and vague aches and pains, he aroused the doctors' curiosity because he silently and persistently turned his back to the ward, shunning any contact with other patients. He was cooperative but neither friendly nor unfriendly, and looked almost devoid of emotion. His history revealed that he grew up in an impoverished Southern Appalachian district. He had left home in his teens, severing his ties with family and neighbors except for very occasionally corresponding with his mother. He remembered that when he was a child, his mother had cried a good deal, and had been in poor health and had had numerous operations. The Army, where he played in a band, became a second home for ten years, until he resigned with the idea of getting more musical training. But he left music school for a menial job, believing that he had too little talent and feeling out of place among the young students. He had never married or had close friends, and was now living alone in one room.

Although patients of this kind give the impression that they lack interest in their environment, they are not as self-sufficient as they appear. Their autonomy is a lifelong protective shield of avoidance and denial, covering the fear of being hurt, upset, and disappointed in personal relationships.

Some of the more fragile individuals among the schizoid personalities are predisposed to severe mental illnesses, usually falling within the group of schizophrenic psychoses. The differential diagnosis between extreme forms of adolescent crisis, schizoid personality, and incipient schizophrenia may require careful observation over a period of time by psychiatrists and clinical psychologists especially experienced with "borderline" cases (Knight, 1953; Gitelson, 1958).

Schizophrenia as a major psychosis lies outside the framework of our discussion, except for those etiological factors which throw some light on the origin of the schizoid personality. Thus far the widespread research into the causes of schizophrenia points to elements in the organic constitution of the infant as well as in his nurturing environment. Suggestive evidence for the influence of heredity is found statistically in a high incidence of concomitance of schizophrenia among identical, one-egg twins and ordinary siblings (Kallman, 1953).

The histories of children with schizophrenia or schizophrenic-like illnesses disclose physiological disturbances, some dating from the beginning of life; among them are: irregular responses and uneven development in motor and postural functions; extremes of overreaction and underreaction of the autonomic nervous system; loss of normal, rhythmic patterns of sleeping, eating, and elimination; and irregularities of physical growth (Bender, 1947; Fish, 1959). Some observers noted the existence, from birth on, of special vulnerabilities such as oversensitivity to incoming stimuli which expose the child to unmanageable overburdening of his central nervous system and lead eventually to a protective withdrawal (Bergman and Escalona, 1949). Some infants seem incapable of reaching out, smiling, and establishing a close emotional contact with their mothers (Kanner, 1942-1943). In another group, a disturbance in the form of extreme inability to separate themselves emotionally from their mothers appears after the first year, when the children normally would begin more and more to test reality and to gain autonomy and independence (Mahler, 1952).

The effects of unusual environmental stress are seen in many instances where the schizoid wariness of any close human relationship is the consequence of many disappointments in the individual's earliest childhood efforts to establish a secure, loving attachment to another person. These disappointments may have been gross, e.g., repeated and prolonged separations from mother, or more insidious, e.g., a lack of warm, steady, and appropriate emotional response from the environment, as is the case when the mother suffers from a severe personality disorder (Rank, 1949).

Studies of families of schizophrenic patients show the pathogenic impact throughout childhood and adolescence of serious difficulties involving both parents, including parental absence, incompatibility, emotional instability and irrationality: besides adversely affecting the child's autonomy, these family disturbances impair the integration of the growing child's personality, his ability to think realistically, communicate, plan and learn, and prevent him from finding a place in the larger community and culture (Lidz, Fleck, and Cornelison, 1965). A special factor, namely, the effect of identification with a deviant environment, is seen clearly in some eccentric, schizoid persons who had an unusual upbringing, in a socially isolated or culturally exceptional group.

When illness intrudes upon the schizoid personality, forcing him to turn for help to others, it threatens to break down his barriers against personal involvement and ensuing disappointments. He may safeguard himself by increasing his denial of problems and by becoming even more seclusive. This unsociability should be respected by the doctor as a necessary protective attitude. At the same time, we must not overlook the patient's needs, nor can we allow him to avoid and reject essential care. He must be given considerate attention, without intruding upon him, and we must not expect him to respond with appreciation to our interest. With cognizance of his deeper oversensitivity we are not as likely to be taken aback if he misinterprets a question or recommendation as meddling, but instead we are prepared to explain our position and responsibility, and to persist cautiously in our continued medical care.

SUGGESTED READING

PUBERTY AND ADOLESCENCE

Blos, P. (1962), *On Adolescence* (New York: Free Press of Glencoe). A comprehensive presentation of normal adolescence with an extensive bibliography.

Deutsch, H. (1967), *Selected Problems of Adolescence* (New York: International Universities Press).

Erikson, E. H. (1959), *Identity and the Life Cycle* [*Psychological Issues*, Monogr. 1] (New York: International Universities Press).

Freud, A. (1936), *The Ego and the Mechanisms of Defense* (New York: International Universities Press, rev. ed., 1966), especially Chapters XI and XII.

Freud, A. (1958), Adolescence. *The Psychoanalytic Study of the Child*, 13:255-278.

Part IV
ADULT LIFE

LECTURE

9

Adult Adaptation: Some Characteristic Forms in Men

Abiding solutions of conflict become apparent in the latter part of adolescence when the typical turbulence has begun to recede. Rooted in the earlier phases of childhood, the kind of personality structure likely to emerge is often foreshadowed before puberty and is already discernible in adolescence. The healthy reaction of the boy leads to his relinquishing the vestiges of his infantile attachment to his mother, its replacement by active desire for girls of his own age, and the reinforcement of his masculine identifications.

When development leads to neurotic solutions, we find a variety of inhibitions and symptoms. We see young men, for example, who cannot be sexually attracted to "nice" girls because they resemble too closely important childhood figures, but who can experience sexual desire only for "bad" women. Another version of the same problem, to avoid sexual relationships which are unconsciously felt to be incestuous, is seen in men who are unable to fall in love with girls of the same social group or religious faith: their fear eventually directs them outside of the "clan." When they marry, their sexual inhibition often takes the form of certain types of hesitancy or impotence, reactions that express the old, unresolved child-

153

hood fears centering around masturbation and forbidden wishes: the fear of having destroyed the power and strength of one's sexual organ. Typically, these young men react this way only with their wives who represent sacred mother figures, but may be potent with other women who are less idealized and at the same time less forbidden.

This was the case with a patient who remained a bachelor for a long time, having devoted himself to his widowed mother. He eventually married a distinguished, motherly woman who was three years older than he, and asked his mother to live with them. His sexual relation to his wife stopped almost completely after a few years of marriage, but his tender affection for her and his thoughtful concern increased proportionately. He never entertained a critical thought or said a harsh word against his wife. He adored her and after his mother's death he used to call her "Mother." At the same time as he gave up his sexual interest in her, he established a satisfactory and intense, intimate relationship with a much younger, much less sophisticated girl, which he maintained for many years alongside the deep asexual devotion to his wife. When this extramarital relationship finally broke up, he lost his emotional equilibrium and developed severe neurotic anxieties. This man showed the signs of an over-attachment to his mother which interfered severely with his normal marital relationship. He could maintain his emotional balance for such a long period only by his splitting his love between the revered motherly kind of woman and the young, sexually desirable girl.

Finally, there is a type of boy who because of his unconscious fear goes even further; he gives up his forbidden aims completely, not only withdrawing from his mother as the love object of his unconscious wishes, but rejecting women altogether. He turns increasingly toward his father and toward men, and his love for them becomes the only acceptable outlet for his drives. This represents one characteristic form of male homosexuality.

A homosexual patient, Mr. P., demonstrated clearly the unconscious mechanism underlying his conscious complete indifference toward women (G. Bibring, 1940). He was convinced that his condition was due to a congenital deficiency which he attributed solely to an organic abnormality. However, we discovered that it was not just lack of interest in women—it was much more than that. He complained that he never recognized a woman whom he had met socially when he encountered her again. He just could not remember women's faces, even if he had spent a whole evening in interesting conversation with them. It was precisely this extreme reaction of his which permitted the therapist to show Mr. P. for the first time that this feeling might not be the result of indifference. If it were just indifference, it would not take such an extreme form and he certainly would remember the face of one or another girl. He was forced to block women out completely, much more than if they simply were of no importance or significance to him. When Mr. P. first came into therapy he described his mother as unworthy of the attention of his father and wondered that such a wonderful man would stay with this woman. In reality, as it turned out, his mother was a rather attractive person, somewhat subdued by her willful and tyrannical husband. Mr. P. could establish a positive relationship to other women only when in the course of psychoanalytic treatment he rediscovered the true, beloved childhood image of the mother behind the layers of his conscious, disparaging attitudes toward her.

In childhood many homosexual men were strongly attached to their mothers and did not establish a firm masculine identification. Their mothers appeared to have been over-solicitous and overinvolved with these little boys, treating them almost like girls, shielding them from any venturesome boys or rough games. Their fathers were often absent, emotionally remote, overcritical, or even openly rejecting toward their sons. The boys frequently turned with affection and erotic feelings to older brothers. In their adolescent or adult homosexual life, they may seek athletic, tough partners with strong masculine characteristics, who have qualities they believe are lacking in themselves and unobtainable for them.

In other cases the little boy's affectionate attachment to his mother persists and may later be transferred to older women friends and patronesses, the man showing no desire to establish a sexual or even tender relationship with younger women. Finally, there is the type of homosexual who loves young boys in a motherly, protective way. This may result from a special resolution of the early childhood love for mother in which these feelings lead to an identification with her instead of the usual masculine identification with father and the search for a female partner.

At the apparent opposite pole from men with sexual inhibitions—if we judge them only by overt symptomatic behavior—we find the "Don Juan" who goes from woman to woman in a constant, futile search for the one he can love truly, who will give him security and rest, and who will fulfill his old, deeply repressed longing for an idealized mother figure. His excesses are a weapon against his anxieties concerning women. The insatiability of his need to bolster his self-regard through sexual "success" points to the persistence of his early infantile insecurities. In another group of ostensibly self-assured men, neurotic anxiety is mixed with fear and contempt of these beings—the women—who are looked down upon as inferior, and at the same time are regarded as dangerous, almost witchlike figures. Such men tend to be domineering and never have a free and natural relation to women, never look at them as equals or partners, but have to prove their own manliness by emphasizing their masculine superiority and by keeping the women down. Thus they reassure themselves that they are safely in the possession of the male role. They seem to fear unconsciously that the "inferior" women won't be kept in their place, that they may rebel against their masters and in some secret way even take revenge upon men or destroy them. Often they can only establish relationships with women who themselves suffer from neurotic feelings of inferiority, presenting the well-known picture of a marriage between an overbearing, domineering husband and an insecure, submissive wife.

We have already encountered, in our discussion of the hysterical personality, men who characteristically emphasize their masculinity. In clinical practice these traits of displaying one's physical strength and competitive triumphs over other men, and one's sexual prowess and domination over women, are often found blended unobtrusively with other qualities.

This was found in the case of a man in his early sixties who suffered an acute, severe myocardial infarction. Mr. R. was a busy designer and builder of precision tools. Besides his business which kept him active enough, he also had a number of hobbies and taught an evening class. He was very considerate and protective of his attractive and equally active wife. His heart attack, which occurred at home, was extremely painful. He was quickly hospitalized. At that time he neither felt especially frightened nor worried about the outcome: he knew that he must die one day, was always prepared, and planned accordingly for his family. Nevertheless, he was comforted by the doctor's ministrations—because he knew that "the medical wheels have started to turn." He also felt some optimism: "Either a heart attack kills you right away or there is hope." After the first few days, when his pain left, he felt in "wonderfully good spirits" and soon began to chafe under the strict regime of rest. It was difficult, he said, because he was so used to being active, but he would curb his impatience and abide by orders until two weeks were up, a time limit tentatively set by his doctor. Then he would demand some concessions. He would have liked more definite information about his progress and the findings of his tests. He wondered if other men with heart attacks are allowed to be active sooner and whether the doctor thought he had too severe an attack to be told, but "I am a man who can take it." At the same time, he expressed confidence in his physician: "Once I put myself in his hands I let him do as he wants." When he was allowed to watch television and read, he became less restive. He believed that lying in bed weakened him: he asked whether the heart is not a muscle that needs exercise. Secretly, he had been moving his fingers and toes and twisting about a little.

The nurses found him a friendly, likable man who seemed to know more about what was going on than most patients, and who realized he was making progress and was bearing up with the regimen. They observed that he was always grinning, talked a lot about his accomplishments, and liked to be the center of attention. He only appeared tense and worried about small things, but never raised his voice. Although he was very eager to go home, he wanted to have everything right before he left the hospital.

Mr. R.'s history showed that his early home life had been quiet and happy. He felt close to both parents, but especially to his mother. As a small boy he had been weak and delicate, and his mother had given him special attention. A turning point came when she took him to a health resort. From then on he engaged himself in all kinds of sports, remaining active all his life until the time of his illness. The father had a small machine and repair shop where the patient enjoyed playing and later working. When he was still a schoolboy his father died suddenly and it turned out that the family was left without any financial resources. For a number of years the patient struggled hard in order to regain some financial security for himself and his family. He married a girl in her teens and showed toward his wife the same devotion which he always maintained toward his mother. In turn his wife idealized him and catered to his needs, and the marriage was exceptionally harmonious.

From the standpoint of his personality we would say that Mr. R.'s self-control, systematic planfulness, and consideration of others were outstanding. Except when he was in pain, he smiled easily, even in the midst of his dangerous illness. His concept of manliness featured physical strength and activity and the overcoming of handicaps and obstacles. Everyone noted how frequently he referred to his achievements. There was a letdown in these defenses after his return home. His near-heroic strength, which had served so well during the acute crisis of illness, was worn down by daily confrontation with the limitations imposed by his condition. As he prepared gradually to resume his work, he felt shaky and weak and appeared somewhat depressed. He complained sadly that he was not allowed to do anything. He thought about death: "Before this I was a young man and all of a sudden I am old." Now he blamed himself for bringing on his coronary by extra exertion and neglecting to take a proper rest the day it happened. This depressive mood lifted only after many months of readjustment. It is interesting to compare this patient with another man who reacted in a different way to an equally severe myocardial infarction.

Mr. T., a fifty-five-year-old insurance agent, became a difficult behavior problem during the first week of his stay in the hospital. He complained vociferously in a blustering way about the care he received, constantly turned his radio up to the loudest level, and placed himself in great danger by refusing to remain at rest. An episode of brief cardiac arrest was precipitated by his exertions. He was anxious to impress everyone with his abilities and accomplishments. He said that he had been very athletic, had never been sick a day in his life, and had always done everything by himself, refusing the help of others. He was especially proud of his accomplishments in certain areas of health insurance, a topic on which he had lectured all across the country.

There was more than a hint that Mr. T. tended to exaggerate these achievements. For example, at first he gave the impression that he was about to be appointed to an important executive position, but later it turned out that he had only corresponded with one of the directors of the company. In discussing his work, he returned again and again to the theme of "protecting lives," and we had the impression that despite his disregard of medical precautions, he was indirectly expressing concern over his own serious heart condition. Another aspect of his anxiety was revealed in an odd way: he mentioned that he had developed a new protective type of garment in which the genitals of athletes would not be exposed to any injury. An important factor in the development of his attitudes was to be found in the residuals of an early attack of poliomyelitis. He was very ashamed of this physical weakness, which he tried to conceal from the nurses. As a youngster he had gone out for a number of sports with a fierce determination to beat everyone despite his handicap.

To help him calm down and accept the necessary restrictions, the staff acknowledged how difficult it was for a man as vigorous as the patient to be placed at bed rest, and how it would take a great deal of strength and effort on his part to go against his nature and lie quietly while his heart heals. He was told that in an illness of this sort the doctors have to depend on the patient, and his recovery was very much in his own control. Further, he was told that they counted upon his understanding since both he and the doctors were in the business of protecting lives. With this approach he became cooperative and the crisis passed.

This patient resembled Mr. R., the toolmaker, in demonstrating his accomplishments and in his insistence upon the importance of muscular strength—both had overcome early physical handicaps. But Mr. T. was much more impulsive, acting out his conflict instead of maintaining self-control. He differed from Mr. R. in another important respect, which leads us to consider a different personality type. He stood out in the extent to which he exaggerated his self-importance and denied any illness or dependence upon others. In medical practice we frequently see people, both men and women, who strongly reject and disavow any personal vulnerability, impairment, or flaw. The person with this response may be supremely self-confident and believe himself to be powerful and important. Like other defensive reactions, this pattern may occur in an acute form, as transient behavior in the face of stress, or it may represent a stabilized personality type. Its most striking pathological form could be seen in the patient with delusions of his own grandeur, while more commonly it may become manifest only as a feeling of superiority.

This attitude was observed in a seventy-year-old laborer, who was critically ill with severe bronchial asthma. He revealed that for many years he had been a "healer" who had the power to cure people of diseases by laying his hands upon them. During the most acute phase of his sickness he showed no fear about his condition and, in fact, went so far as to reject the idea that he was ill at all, regarding his hospitalization as a kind of punishment from God for having been too proud and having neglected to relieve those who needed his help. At the same time his denial of the underlying dread of the danger of illness was revealed by his constant preoccupation with his remarkable "ability" to restore invalids to health, almost literally as if he could bring them back from the very jaws of death. Apparently he succeeded in this way to ward off his anxiety; in any event, it did not lead to particular problems in the medical management as it often does with patients who have this sort of self-image.

This kind of defense against extreme anxiety by denial and by overcompensatory omnipotent fantasies can be found at any age, but is common in response to developmental crisis such as adolescence or aging. Both traumatic and developmental stresses were at work in the case of Neil, the adolescent football hero (Lecture 8). He showed, in an intense form, denial of the prospect of leg amputation. The operation represented a most severe attack upon his image of himself as a strong man. Similarly, reactions of this kind are evoked in many aging men when their masculine position or their ability to lead an independent life is threatened. We can understand these responses and traits in part as an exaggeration of normal self-respect. The forerunner of this excessive self-regard is to be found in early childhood when so great a proportion of the baby's interest is directed to his own needs and comforts, and he is cherished by an adoring family—before the child's experience of the limitations set by reality modifies this elevated self-esteem. Borrowing from the Greek myth of the youth Narcissus who fell in love with his own reflection, we designate persons in whom attitudes of self-love and superiority are predominant as being *narcissistic*.

Frequently when an individual of this type is ill he will deem only the most eminent physician worthy of attending him, choosing someone who reinforces his own sense of perfection. For example, on the hospital ward a narcissistic man will grandly announce and emphasize repeatedly that the Chief of Service—"the professor"—is his doctor; he permits the residents—"the boys"—to examine him only because he believes that they will learn a great deal from him. However, having selected a sufficiently distinguished doctor whose competence he can admire, this type of person will then often compete with him, search out his weaknesses, and dwell upon his slightest faults. In addition, this patient may alienate the staff by seeming smug, vain, arrogant, or egocentric, or by displaying the air of "knowing it all." We must recognize that the narcissistic patient has to look upon himself as an expert and wants to believe that his own views carry more weight than do mere medical recommendations.

Thus in order to avoid unnecessary and disturbing tensions it is essential that we have sufficient tolerance for this person's defensive armor and appreciate his points of view as long as they do not interfere grossly with rational medical management. In doing this we should not go so far as to minimize our own expert knowledge and skill, for our own sake and for the sake of the patient who, in spite of all his efforts to discover our shortcomings, is deeply afraid, like any other patient, that he might not get the best available medical care.

10

Adult Adaptation: Some Characteristic Forms in Women

The narcissistic feeling of superiority is found in both women and men, though women seem to find it more difficult to cover up its deeper counterpart, the neurotic feeling of inferiority. This will be understood better after a more detailed discussion of the girl's adolescence and her further development, both in its normal and maladaptive forms. In adolescence the well-adjusted girl is ready to give up her childhood attachment to her father, to replace her early ideal of him as the only man who counts by other suitable figures, and to want to marry and become a mother herself. She is not alarmed or repelled by menstruation or by the thought of intercourse, pregnancy, and childbirth; she awaits these experiences with a certain natural apprehension, but at the same time she feels pride in her female role and functions. For her, the first menstruation is like a promise, not like a "curse," as it is for many women who, in their common negative reaction to it, introduced this expression into everyday language. Yet if a psychologically healthy woman does not marry or is unable to have children, she will not break down but will be able to stand the disappointment and to establish for herself a satisfactory life which will help her accept the necessary renunciation. However, as doctors we also have to deal with women who were not as successful in maturing into healthy adults.

In a manner similar to the reactions of adolescent boys, neurotic behavior in girls may appear at the one extreme as overstrict prohibition and denial combined with sexual inhibition and frigidity, as if no man were permitted and nothing is admitted in the girl's life that reminds her of being female or having sexual needs. And at the other extreme we find girls who act impulsively in a promiscuous way. People mistakenly tend to assume that promiscuous women, especially prostitutes, are predominantly uninhibited individuals with strong sexual drives. Impulsive behavior on this basis is found mainly in girls who grew up in a sexually uninhibited environment or were subjected to early sexual seduction, in girls who lack normal inhibitions due to constitutional and organic defects as in mental defectives or deteriorated alcoholics, or in girls who have borderline or psychotic disturbances. But more often the behavior of wayward and delinquent patients is the result of unconscious conflicts between drives and inhibitions, leading to neurotic acting out in this form. Even when the sexual activity looks like a direct instinctual fulfillment, it is often compulsive and accompanied by unconscious guilt feelings: it is an incomplete and distorted or displaced gratification and by no means what it seems to be, a simple satisfaction of wishes and fantasies. Many prostitutes are as frigid as the completely inhibited, "asexual" type of women. They conspicuously lack the strong attachment to the sexual partner that is the result of real, full sexual gratification. And in a kind of vicious circle, because they miss the deepening of love, the commitment and loyalty that are fostered by mutual contentment, their capacity for sexual enjoyment is limited and replaced by frustration and aggressive resentment.

Another neurotic trend in the development of women often follows the form of the girl's early reactions to the discovery of sexual anatomical differences. The little girl who is contending with the problem of her bodily difference, who struggles with many feelings of being passed over, of envy and self-devaluation, may cling to the idea that she is really a boy who has lost his genital organ, and thus she will be inclined to comfort herself in her fantasies with the hope that the organ will grow again. She is used to hearing that most of the things she wants to get will come later, that she will go to parties or buy her own nice clothes or cook what she likes when she is grown up. Thus the girl may try to keep to that idea with regard to her genitals too: they will grow in time.

If the girl cannot convince herself that everything will be all right because a sense of guilt interferes with this fantasy, if there is a vague fear that she is to blame for her "defect"—perhaps related to masturbation or to resentful, aggressive wishes toward her mother or her "preferred" little brothers—then she may be left with a feeling of inferiority about her "deformed" body and her whole personality. Or she may turn to her mother for reparation and experience a growing disappointment because no help is forthcoming. She may react with outspoken hostility toward her mother as well as toward the favored boys, and be unable to find a way out of this conflict; or she may indignantly deny the whole problem of her femininity, never accepting it as a fact. Some girls, in defiance and in order to comfort themselves, turn to an artificial and exaggerated appreciation for the rest of their body, trying to find compensation in its beauty. These hopeful or self-depreciative, vengeful or compensatory reactions, insignificant as they may seem, can become the center of different types of specific feminine difficulties: if they meet with strong tendencies in the girl toward activity, they represent the basis of what is often called the "masculinity complex." The girl will soon forget these original reactions, repressing the memory of them, but we can see their influence exerted from within, shaping her personality, affecting her reactions to her feminine functions, and contributing to her future success or neurotic failure as a woman.

To elaborate on these varied reactions in some detail: the first response we mentioned is the hopeful one: "I surely will change, it will come. I will be like the boys." This hope and confidence, if preserved unconsciously, may have the following effect: the girl may turn into a little tomboy without showing much interest in a girl's likes and occupations, always be among boys, always one of the first among them, if possible quicker, braver, more daring than the boys. Although this overachieving betrays some persistent doubts rather than complete and unshakable confidence in her fantasies, it serves the exaggerated need to reassure herself that her hopes are justified. The persistence of this conflict does not necessarily lead to serious disturbances, but it can result in characteristic personality traits. She might grow up into a very active person who by preference will tend to concentrate on and compete in intellectual areas usually chosen by men, and she will strive to excel in performance that requires courage and enterprise. She is often good company for men, who regard her as a "pal" or "buddy." Yet with it goes a certain lack of soft, feminine qualities, which she suppresses in her aversion toward the "inferiority of the woman." The same prejudice prevents her from enjoying women, whom she usually dislikes, finding them silly or petty.

The girl who feared that she lost perfection by her own fault later reacts with unhappiness and depressive moods. Her original complaint, that boys have a better, more impressive and superior body, now takes the form of envious admiration for men's achievements, be they intellectual, athletic, or artistic. This then results in the girl's feeling of inferiority and her inability to accomplish anything in these areas. Many symptoms like learning difficulties, helplessness when faced with a task, or extreme silliness in young girls may be the expression of this persistent problem. It is as if she said, "I am not a fine boy. I am incapable of thinking. I am only a foolish girl." Here, we suppose, one can easily anticipate the picture of certain women, perpetually dissatisfied with themselves, full of self-depreciation, with an exaggerated bias in favor of anything masculine. Among these women we find the extreme type mentioned before, who shows complete submissiveness in her marriage. She complements an authoritarian, domineering husband, and both of them take this aspect of their marriage for granted.

The case of a very interesting and attractive-looking, married woman of twenty-five, the mother of a two-year-old boy, may serve to demonstrate the combination of these reactions, the tomboyish hope of achieving masculine integrity, together with the anxiety of the girl who fears that she may remain inferior. Mrs. U. was in an intellectual profession for which she showed outstanding talent. She complained of difficulties in her relationship to her husband, of whom she was very fond and whom she admired but without ever having felt any deep love for him, though he was the first and only man in her life. She was frigid sexually and accepted her husband's approach in order not to hurt him. Lately there were also difficulties in her professional work where she knew that she could achieve more, but felt quite disturbed and inhibited whenever she started to settle down to it. She then reacted with a feeling of despair and depression, though she did not give up her hope for success, expecting that she might achieve something of importance one day. This struggle between her determination and the inner obstacles exhausted her in her professional tasks.

Another of her difficulties concerned her son. She had wanted the child, but here too she felt that she did not really love him. When they were together she worried about neglecting her work. When working she felt guilty about neglecting her child. Sometimes these conflicts seemed overwhelming: she knew that her life could be perfect and easy, and yet, nevertheless, it was a succession of worries and disappointments. She had gone through a rather deep depression after the birth of her baby and, being pregnant again, she decided to see the doctor in the hope of preventing a recurrence of this unhappy condition.

Mrs. U. was the youngest of four children, having three older brothers. They all had remained close friends. Her father was an intelligent, interesting, and very understanding man, of the highest moral standards. The mother had little influence on the children and was not quite of his superior caliber. The patient had no special conflict with her mother, but there was a marked difference in her attitude toward her father and toward her mother, and she soon recognized that her father had always been her ideal. Her childhood dream was to become like him or her oldest brother. She was invariably irritated when her mother criticized her boyish behavior, her modesty in clothes, or her lack of interest in young men. She was a brilliant student, hardworking and dedicated. While attending university she met her present husband. He was one of the instructors and all the students thought very highly of him. After they married she proved to be frigid. During the first months she cried a great deal without knowing why, and always tried to hide her tears because they seemed a shameful weakness.

Mrs. U. reported two interesting neurotic symptoms which had worried her very much around the time of puberty. The first was something difficult to believe in a youngster so honest and high-principled, something that she had struggled against with all her might, but without success for quite some time. She had suffered from kleptomanic impulses. She had stolen books from bookstores and public libraries, though her allowance was more than sufficient to buy them. And she described her emotions when stealing as a mixture of complete despair, fear, and the greatest excitement that she had ever felt either before or afterward. She finally was able to overcome this impulse after she had been caught once. The librarian seemed to understand that this girl was not a regular thief. He did not fuss too much about it, but admonished her not to continue these dangerous acts as they could spoil her entire future. After this encounter she never did it again.

The second symptom was a tormenting and completely "nonsensical" compulsion of the following kind: if a girl or woman expressed an opinion like, "I love this concert," or "Democracy is the desirable form of government," or any other statement of this kind, the patient forced herself to imagine that this was not said by this particular girl but by a boy. She had to think hard, to shift the situation, until, in her inner mind, she heard these words spoken by a male. Then she had to ask herself, "Does this now have the same meaning or does it mean more?" "Would it sound more significant or not?" The opposite took place when a boy made a remark such as "It will rain soon." She had to imagine those words being spoken by a girl, and then had to ask herself whether it would now sound silly or just as objective and matter-of-fact as it had before when the boy had said it.

The patient herself felt that this symptom had some connection with important questions in her mind. She had always been concerned with comparing men and women, and had always been inclined to find that men are superior, better, more objective, or more sincere. At the same time she worried about herself: whether she would turn out an equal to men or whether she might perhaps turn into one of those superficial girls, whom she avoided so systematically. Her school friends, for instance, were all of her own type, good, serious students, and none of them had ever been frivolous or played around with boys. And after she had told all this, she suddenly, with a shock, remembered a strange incident which had been completely forgotten and which, as she recalled now, marked the beginning of a third symptom.

Once when she was sixteen, her oldest brother, who then served in the Army, came home on leave. The patient with two girlfriends planned something very special for him: they were going to take the young officer out in the evening. He was very surprised and amused by this special party in his honor, and they all went to a nice restaurant on the outskirts of the city. It was summer, and everything about the occasion seemed so unusual to our patient: the wine, the type of entertainment, the atmosphere between the young man and her friends. When they went back, they all stood on the open platform of the small country railway station, the patient a little bit tipsy but very controlled, and slightly uneasy because she felt the need to urinate. As usual, she felt too inhibited to go to the toilet when friends could take notice of it; she had a general habit of postponing this to test her self-control. The humor among the young people became more and more personal, and there was clearly an erotic interplay between her brother and her girlfriends. She observed this, a little dazed by the alcohol, without much antagonism but with a slight feeling of superiority: she surely would not be caught so easily by the handsome face of a young officer.

Mrs. U. could see herself standing there, in an attack of strange depersonalization—as if all this were happening not to her but to someone else—staring at her brother's sword, which was hanging down from his belt. And all at once, without any possibility of moving or doing anything about it, she started to urinate more and more, endlessly it seemed, standing on the platform among her friends. In the general excitement of their conversation nobody observed it. The patient described the feeling as a mixture of extreme strain and faint pleasure, which afterward gave way to desperate self-reproaches for this shameful weakness. Ever since then she suffered from urinary frequency which at times was quite troublesome.

After Mrs. U. had told the story, she was on the verge of tears. She had prided herself on being, on the whole, a healthy and balanced person, and now she had to discover all these "crazy" and abnormal symptoms and experiences. But as we gave thought to the unconscious meaning of these symptoms, different as they all seemed, we could discern that in reality they represented one and the same unconscious conflict, expressed in different ways and in different disguises.

I shall permit myself to leave out the details and present only the conclusion at which we arrived: this patient's early childhood reaction was: "I am a girl and I hate to be one, it is inferior and degrading, it is like mother, and I hope I will change and be as intelligent and superior as my beloved brothers and father." For her, intelligence became a substitute for the missing organ. In adolescence this fantasy was revived and led to the three neurotic symptoms. One expressed her fears, doubts, and feelings of inferiority: "Can women think as objectively and as significantly as men?" "Does it hold good when a woman says something?" "Could it have been said by a man, too, or is there an unbridgeable difference between them?"

The second symptom, her kleptomanic impulse, was a typical symptom for a girl with her unconscious problem and wishes. It was neither an attempt to gain a material advantage, nor was it done *pour épater les bourgeois;* rather her unconscious longing to possess a penis had been displaced onto the wish to have a man's intellectual prowess. For her, books and knowledge and intelligence stood for masculinity, and this is what created the strange urge to snatch these books away from where they belonged and make them her own possession. It is interesting and can be understood from this explanation that kleptomania, like shoplifting, is almost exclusively limited to women.

The third symptom, the urinary frequency dating from her lapse of self-control in an erotic adolescent atmosphere, began with an almost undisguised breakthrough of her wish for the male organ. As she looked at her much admired, uniformed oldest brother, gazing at his sword and observing his success with her girlfriends, the conflict between her competitive masculine wishes and her devalued female tendencies emerged. It was expressed in a typical compromise as a symptom, which, on the one hand, represented the childhood

memory of the boy who urinates in a standing position showing off in front of the girl; on the other hand, it portrayed
the helplessness of the weak and defective female.

In the light of this interpretation, the difficulties which
brought her to the therapist do not surprise us: Mrs. U. had
never genuinely accepted the woman's role for herself. She
had married a man for whom she felt affection because he was
a capable and decent fellow, but she had never felt any erotic
excitement in her marriage with him. Sexuality hardly existed
for her; she was frigid. Childbirth, as a decisive confirmation
of femininity, drove her into a deep depression, almost into
suicide. Her motherly love was disturbed by her masculine,
intellectual strivings. To stay with the child meant giving up
her highest professional goals, but at the same time there was a
strong, repressed feeling of love for the baby and a compelling
sense of responsibility which did not permit her to shake off
her duty and neglect her son. She felt that she was equally
unfair to him and her husband, on the one hand, and to her
work, on the other: in addition, deep down she never over-
came her doubts about her boyish hopes, and this insecurity
interfered further with the strongest symbol of masculinity,
her intellectual pursuits.

To examine another characteristic response that a girl
might have to the discovery of her female body, we now turn
to the girl who is unable to overcome her hostility toward her
mother, and her extremely jealous and resentful attitude
toward the "favored" boys. In the child the discovery might
lead to a sudden behavior problem such as naughtiness toward
her mother, and quarrelsomeness and aggressiveness toward
boys. But if this continues into adult life, the results are some
rather disturbing symptoms and character traits, afflicting the
woman's relationship to men and affecting her biological
functions. Among them are frigidity, a variety of difficulties
with menstruation and pregnancy, rejection of her child, and
dissatisfaction, competitive hostility, and hypersensitivity

toward men. In some cases the outcome might be a complete rejection of the man, replacing heterosexual with homosexual relationships.

Miss V., forty years of age, exemplified some of these neurotic trends. She was beautiful, elegant, and soignée, and obviously took great care to appear as attractive as possible. She did not look older than thirty. Her complaints referred to depression, unhappiness about getting old, having gray hair (she dyed it platinum blond), and above all to her difficulties with men. She had had a series of affairs since the age of seventeen, but for some reason or other they never led to marriage. She thought it disgraceful for a woman not to be married and she wondered whether something could be wrong with her so that she was unable to find a suitable marital partner. We soon began to learn what the real trouble was about. To summarize: every man who risked loving this attractive and nice-looking woman became involved in her intense conflicts. She was filled with fantasies about men's excessively aggressive behavior. Her ideas were: "A woman is a poor, inferior creature, and men know this. A man only uses her for his sexual desire, and then laughs at her and leaves her in disgrace. He wanders off, whistling, with a feather in his cap." This was the expression she constantly used. Men were like the boys she envied as a child, when they went off on their bicycles while she had to stay with mother.

She was next to the youngest in a family of eight children, three boys and five girls. When she was four years old, the following traumatic events happened: her oldest brother, whose favorite she had been, left the house for good after a violent scene with her father and was never heard from again; the father, who had been a very happy and friendly man, always singing and laughing and whistling, died suddenly in an accident a few weeks later: "All men leave their women with broken hearts and wander off whistling and unconcerned." She did not understand the fate of these two beloved men at that time, as we can see: for her, it was a heartless, purposeful act, directed against the poor little girl and against all women—because her mother was really left in despair by father's death, with six children and another on the way. The mother gave birth to a girl two months later and almost died of hemorrhage. There was no money, only illness, tears, and unhappiness: "and the women stay alone in disgrace and have to suffer for their stupid love." How often might the girl have heard similar remarks from her desperate mother, who had a violent temper and was inclined to abuse, scold, and complain.

At this time, because there was no one to look after her, Miss V. had another severe traumatic experience. An exhibitionist approached her in the cellar of her house. The memory of the sight of his organ pursued her up to the day when she went into treatment. It was, in her description, one of the most frightening things imaginable. She had felt completely paralyzed and had had the impression of an enormous, dangerous weapon assaulting her.

Miss V.'s relationship with her mother—the only sustaining figure who could fill the place of her missing brother and father—started to deteriorate during this period and became increasingly intolerable. The girl was intensely jealous, interpreting her mother's attention to the newborn baby as a rejection of herself. In addition, she resented her mother's dependence upon the two remaining older brothers as a sign of preference for the boys. This strengthened her conviction that boys are something better, more precious, and always favored, and aroused in her an overwhelming hatred toward her mother. Everything that went wrong in her life had to be blamed on mother. The patient often made the most fantastic accusations against her, in an orgy of hatred, without any insight or perspective. She thus hated men because "they could do as they pleased and got everything desirable which had been withheld from me." She hated her mother as responsible for this injustice because "mother went along with it instead of making amends for it." She hated herself as a woman because this meant being a failure, a freak, a weak, deserted fool. The only thing she truly loved was her beautiful body, which she admired and cared for as her sole compensation and as her means of attracting men whose attention had such importance for her.

It became apparent that her burning wish was to conquer a man, and to keep him as a kind of prized possession and a challenge to other women, as if to say, "See here, I am not inferior like you; if I am not a man myself, at least I own a man." She treated the men in her fantasies very harshly. She wanted to take revenge for all that she believed they had done to girls, for their arrogance and independence, and especially for their sexual exploitations that caused so much unhappiness to their women. Without being aware of this she tormented the men who established intimate relations with her. She excited them sexually and then suddenly withdrew, hurting them with sarcastic remarks. She set out to break their independence, to agitate them, and to render them impotent. It is quite understandable that men who were interested in her could not tolerate this situation and would soon take flight; she then had to start a new relationship which inevitably repeated the same pattern. And this was the reason why her successes with men did not lead to marriage, but only to a series of promiscuous episodes.

The rather dramatic picture presented by Miss V. includes elements of another characteristic reaction arising from the girl's childhood envy of the boy—an attempt to deny her own defect or shortcoming by looking for compensation within herself. Excessive admiration for her own body can be the outcome of this attempt to compensate for the lack by emphasizing "what has been left to her." Again, the unconscious conflicts reveal themselves in extreme and inappropriate unhappiness over minor failures like having to wear last year's coat, or in the compulsive urge to keep busy with her beauty treatment. This self-concern, including the need that others feast their eyes upon her, is an exaggeration of normal feminine wishes.

The beginning of this attitude can be observed quite easily. We saw a small girl who all at once, after the birth of her baby brother, started to dress herself up, to stand in front of the mirror all day long, and to cry because she wanted another handbag in addition to the three that she had already received. Later, such women may have a special interest in men, but it is channeled into being prized by men for their beauty and is not predominantly an expression of their love for men. It is often of equal importance that they be admired enviously by other women.

When neurotic inhibitions, symptoms, and behavior patterns are observed, psychiatric evaluation will help determine their significance. Deep-seated disturbances require psychoanalysis or intensive psychotherapy. Disorders that are relatively acute, superficial, and likely to respond to clarification of fears and misconceptions, and to reassurance appropriate to the patient's personality, may be treated by the psychiatrist or the informed family physician with brief psychotherapy.

In the case of emotional reactions to physical illnesses, many of the indications for psychological management discussed in previous lectures will be applicable to these patients. Thus, an active tomboy or an overassertive man facing unusual stress situations will often regain a sense of mastery if he recognizes the doctor's confidence in his strength. With the man who is fighting to maintain his self-image of masculinity we cannot always accept this at face value but must proceed with careful attention to the degree of his anxiety. If it appears that our explicit trust in him only increases his tension, like an unmanageable challenge, then we have to take a more protective position.

The doctor must not allow himself to become involved in a struggle with the antagonistic, vengeful kind of woman patient, eventually to be cast in the role of rejecting and abandoning her, but must extricate himself from her provocation with the full understanding that this is her lifelong pattern and not a personal issue. The woman who seems so exceedingly "vain" about her appearance and shows extreme concern over the treatment of a small, benign mole may easily arouse intense irritation in her physician, who is accustomed to caring for truly severe conditions. Nevertheless, for such a patient, her insignificant blemish may represent emotionally a more serious threat than even a major operation. Acknowledgment of her fastidious grooming with the reassurance that this surely outweighs the presence of a small scar will be more effective than scolding her about her frivolous vanity. The psychological management of the woman in whom feelings of inferiority predominate, who is inclined to blame herself for her physical disorder, and who questions whether much can be done to improve her condition, is similar to our approach to the masochistic individual whom we shall consider now.

The type of woman who regards boys and men as superior, who at the same time is envious of them, and who is pessimistic and full of self-depreciation and doubts about her own value, often shows an exquisitely masochistic attitude. The masochistic tendency to seek gratification through suffering, self-sacrifice, or renunciation deserves our special attention because of its complexity, the difficulties in psychological management it usually presents, and because physical symptoms, more than most other stress situations, bring out this seemingly paradoxical reaction. These masochistic personality traits have to be distinguished from masochism as a perversion, a pathological form of manifest sexual behavior in which suffering is an essential condition for gratification; whereas the masochistic trends that we refer to are in no way experienced by the individual as sexual in nature, though they provide in a slightly disguised form an admixture of satisfaction.

For a number of reasons they are seen more frequently in women than in men.

One basic cause lies in the limitation of direct expression of aggressive feelings in girls, partly as a result of their less intense biological urge toward activity and partly due to the environment's pressure and expectation. As a consequence, the girl's aggressive impulses, increasing without adequate discharge, may be turned against herself in the same way that a person with helpless anger might pound his hand until it hurts. When we consider along with this that all of the girl's and woman's sexual functions are characteristically accompanied by discomfort or even pain, as menstruation, intercourse, and childbirth, we can understand that a masochistic component, i.e., a fusion of gratification and suffering, is an intrinsic constituent of the psychology of women.

Such attitudes should be distinguished from the extreme character masochism found in the kind of woman who depreciates herself, who does not expect any success from her efforts, who forces herself to accept anything as good enough for her, and who is inclined to mistreat herself even if nobody else abuses her. This type of masochism is a marked distortion of the biological compliance and passivity of the normal woman. Likewise, the debased conception of femininity in these extreme cases contrasts markedly with the genuine acceptance of her role in an emotionally healthy woman.

Sometimes we are led to recognize masochistic personalities by evidence of their self-sacrificial tendencies, their submissiveness and need to serve other people. Others have a history of repeated distressing experiences which they firmly believe are due to adverse circumstances and bad luck. Upon closer examination of these episodes, we discern that these individuals often precipitate their misfortunes, provoke disappointments, and seek out situations which are likely to turn out unsatisfactorily, or that they respond oversensitively to any form of hardship. Even when it appears that they have volunteered to be of service to others and that no one wants to humiliate them, it is part of their inner pattern and expectation to feel exploited and depreciated.

On the other hand, it can be observed that masochistic individuals may derive feelings of pride and vicarious satisfaction from such a role. In spite of the self-effacing modesty we usually can observe an exhibitionistic element in their behavior; directly or subtly the masochistic person lets his environment know that he is having an extremely hard time or has exhausted his strength for the sake of other people and should get credit for it. Characteristically, these patients evoke sympathy and attentiveness because of what they have to endure. At the same time they arouse uneasiness and a guilty intolerance in others by indirectly conveying the reproach that others could and should do more to acknowledge their sacrifices or to show them their appreciation.

The central feature of masochism, the paradoxical desire to achieve satisfaction through suffering, is contrary to the prevalent notion that only pleasure is sought after and that pain is to be avoided at any price. The picture becomes less puzzling when we look more closely at the relation of pleasure to pain, taking into account some of the deeper psychological forces operative in masochism, and consider further how such a pervasive attitude in the personality may have developed. As we discussed in connection with the masochistic trend in feminine psychology, pleasure and pain are often intimately associated both physiologically and psychologically. We are not unfamiliar with the alternation of tension and release or the mingling and fusion of discomfort and pleasure in the sexual act, in roughhousing play and athletic exertion, and in the bittersweet states of such experiences as lovesickness and "Weltschmerz."

Aggressiveness and guilt feelings are specially important in the dynamics of masochism. Limitation of the outward expression of aggressive feelings, more common in women, was already mentioned as a factor predisposing to masochism. Social agencies have vast experience with masochistic women who have a history of consecutive relationships with several men, alcoholics, delinquents, and deserters, who abuse and maltreat them, from whom they finally separate only to enter the next relationship with a similar type of man. In most of these cases, an unconscious feeling of guilt is an important dynamic factor in their masochistic behavior. Such personalities range from the chronic worrier who always expects setbacks whenever things are going well, through certain types of accident-prone patients, all the way up to what we call the "martyr." The "martyr" believes that his ideals have to be achieved through marked self-sacrifice and suffering. He does not simply take unavoidable adverse experiences in his stride, but glories in them, with the conviction that sacrifice is an essential part of promoting his cause.

Certain early experiences seem to favor accentuation of the masochistic trends. Severely repressive training in which the child was made to feel guilty for even ordinary and harmless expression of sexual and aggressive feelings, and harsh chastisement, especially the use of corporal punishment which may produce excitement tinged with pleasure, are among the causes of this type of character development. Identification with a suffering parent may also be of etiological importance. Or an attachment to a parent who is sadistic toward the child, forcing the youngster to submit to abuse, may shape the child's relationships to important figures in life according to this model. Children often discover how suffering may lead to the satisfaction of otherwise prohibited impulses. They had to learn to control their wish to gain more than their share of love from the parents, but suddenly, when they become sick, they receive all the attention one could hope for, all kinds of dispensation and forgiveness for behavior which had previously brought only reprimands and punishment. Thus, being ill and suffering may become established as successful means of providing fundamental satisfaction. This is another root of masochism, as a special form of what is called the "secondary gain through illness."

Illnesses that wear down patients, like severe recurrent or chronic diseases, conditions requiring massive or multiple surgical procedures, and ailments that cause protracted pain seem particularly prone to release masochistic tendencies. We can readily understand how trying such masochistic attitudes can be for the physician, especially when they appear in the form of reproaches and a definite resistance to being cured or helped and a kind of clinging to misery. The physician should heed the underlying appeal for care and acceptance, but also appreciate that this person does not feel ready to receive help without much suffering. When such a patient says, characteristically, "It's not easy, doctor," he is not asking for encouraging comments but rather wants recognition and acknowledgement of his ordeal. He can cooperate better if you present to him the necessary treatment as an additional effort, almost like shouldering a new burden. It is preferable if this need can be presented to him as benefiting others, his spouse or children or friends, or even as a way of rewarding his doctors for their care and concern, rather than for the personal relief that health would bring to him.

LECTURE

11

Marriage and Pregnancy

Marriage, one of the most important experiences of adult life, is of special concern to the physician. It affects the condition of one's patients in all sorts of ways and marital problems are frequently brought to the doctor before anyone else. With the support of the social environment, marriage permits the meeting of needs for sexual fulfillment, closeness, and reliability and constancy in a relationship without pretense or artificiality. As a "settling down" it provides an efficient stabilization of essential routines and rhythms of satisfaction that can facilitate productive and creative activity in raising children as well as in work. In the normal situation it allows and reflects a further advance in the resolution of the conflicts that arose in the family setting of early childhood. Conversely, it may become an arena for the continuation of the infantile struggle.

You will recall that in the latency period the child was able to carry his strong feelings out of the home and, so to speak, distribute them among other persons such as teachers and schoolmates. Thus a discharge and a mitigation of tensions were made possible. In the adult this process is now reversed at a mature level with the establishment of a new household, which is inevitably reminiscent, in many ways, of the early

183

family situation. Marriage becomes a testing ground of earlier solutions of conflicts. The request for considerate commitment to others, the necessary leveling down of the overidealized image of the love object after the honeymoon period, the sexual adjustment, social and financial responsibilities, and the needs of growing children all contribute to tensions that may be expressed in a variety of different maladaptations and symptoms.

We observe that even people who on the whole are quite thoughtful and considerate may behave in an oddly different way upon entering wedlock; they are inclined to take their personal problems out on each other. Each may try to change the other, disregarding the fact that the partner's personality, like one's own, is the outcome of his or her development and need for equilibrium, and not just a superficial and arbitrary posture which can be dropped upon request. Nor will the partners remain aware of how hurt they themselves would feel if in turn such demands were made upon them to change their own personalities, their needs, and defenses. Not infrequently the in-laws serve as a relatively safe, sufficiently distant focus of dissensions which are displaced from one's own parents or spouse.

The establishment of a truly empathic relationship in marriage is a task of mutual adjustment which touches upon all of the adaptive problems at the different stages of development that we have discussed so far. One of the experiences which shows in a concentrated form the effect exerted by the marital relationship as well as by the earlier life phases is pregnancy with its intricate biopsychological interaction. And this important process influences to a high degree the course of parenthood.

People in general are inclined to look upon pregnancy as a biological event in which everything is well taken care of by nature and which normally will run its course simply and uneventfully. This point of view is rather deceptive in its simplification. Even though the pattern is biologically given, and even though most pregnant women and their environment are consciously unaware of any profound emotional changes which may take place, the step-by-step process is complex and worthy of careful study.

Pregnancy is one of the decisive, irreversible developmental turning points. It is a move toward an exquisitely new constellation, a new role of paramount importance, comparable to an event like puberty or the climacterium—the step from adulthood toward aging: all of these steps in the life cycle have specific psychosomatic significance in the broadest sense of the term; in the sense that changes of equal importance take place somatically and psychologically, and that these changes are mutually dependent, supporting or interfering with each other as the case may be.

When we try to understand and treat the problems and complications of pregnancy, many of which may continue afterward, like difficulties in conceiving, carrying to term, delivering or nursing, hyperemesis, frequent backaches, fatigue, loss of sexual feelings, and depressions, then we must consider both their organic and psychogenic etiology.

As far as the somatic changes are concerned—and we confine ourselves to a basic outline—the characteristic elements in the first trimester are the missing of the menstrual period and the morning nausea due to alterations in gastric secretions and intestinal functioning. Toward the end of the fourth month the expectant mother becomes directly aware of the fetus as it starts to move inside of her, and frequently she experiences a general and continuing sense of relaxed physical well-being.[1] In the latter half of pregnancy, she feels the weight and bulk and pressure of her growing baby and, increasingly, is aware of the changes in her body and its contours. Finally, she faces and performs the task of delivery

[1] According to the interesting psychosomatic studies on *Psychosexual Functions in Women* by Therese Benedek and Boris B. Rubenstein (1952), these physical conditions accompanied by a psychological feeling of passive contentment are linked up with the endocrine changes at this period.

and, with it, separation from the infant, starting him on his way to a relatively independent life.

What are some of the psychological counterparts or aspects of these physiological events? As in the endocrine process where several hormones stimulate and regulate the cycle, psychologically too we have to consider the interplay of different, often diametrically opposed impulses and tendencies whose blending serves the optimum emotional development of the pregnant woman, leading to the desirable readiness for motherhood. Basic among these urges and trends are her concern, interest, and preoccupation turned toward herself and toward the changes taking place within her, which must be reconciled with her interest and love for others, particularly for her husband and the coming baby as a person to be loved: her impulses to approach the world actively are in conflict with her passive wishes to be taken care of and with the special necessity to await and to submit to the course of events during pregnancy.

And, as an understanding of the somatic condition of the pregnant woman requires that we consider the whole history of her endocrine functions and the complete preparatory somatic phase of her female development from the time she was a little girl, so must we take into account, when studying the psychology of the pregnant female, her entire psychological development. This comprises the phases of infancy, including the effect her mother's care had on her healthy psychological development, and leads via the preparation in childhood for puberty and becoming a woman, through all the experiences of adjusting to menstruation and sexual relations, to the desire of being a woman and mother herself. This wish means that she wants to receive her husband, to take care of someone as a mother, to have a child of her own, but with it, to want this child, this part of herself, to separate finally and to grow up toward individual independence.

However, certain concepts pertaining to female biology, like menstruation and pregnancy, are charged with a variety of unconscious connotations based upon naïve ideas occurring in childhood concerning bleeding, the unknown interior of the body, and where babies come from. In addition, archaic ideas and shadowy feelings stemming from the girl's earliest relationship to her own mother seem to emerge during pregnancy. When we observe them at this time, they seem incongruous with the prevailing, manifestly placid and optimistic attitude of most women. And yet, such ideas and emotions, which are mostly deeply repressed in the woman, are frequently close to awareness in pregnancy.

The apprehension and sense of mystery associated with menstruation, sexual intercourse, pregnancy, and miscarriage, which are found in dreams, fantasies, and neurotic fears, are regular features of the beliefs of primitive peoples and the superstitions of more civilized ones. Among savage tribes the possessions, the touch, and particularly the blood of menstruating women are tabooed as polluted and deadly. It is as if genital bleeding stirred up unconscious fears surrounding the ideas of mutilation and castration. And in more advanced societies, ignorant and credulous people believe that a menstruating woman can make beer, wine, milk, or jam go bad, blight crops, dim mirrors, rust iron, and raise storms at sea. To the minds of children, bleeding suggests internal destruction of the body, and this idea reinforces and becomes part of masochistic fantasies and castration anxiety. In accordance with the girl's unsolved unconscious anxieties, bleeding may primarily be regarded as further evidence of loss of her male genital organ and of damage and punishment for early masturbation, or the blood may represent a dirty, anal waste product, or, in terms of oral preoccupations, a poisonous and pestilential substance.

Normally, therefore, the baby growing within the mother may have the significance of a reward for accepting the feminine role (which, as a matter of fact, it is) or, in the extreme opposite case of unsolved resentment over her unacceptable biological position, the fetus may represent a cancer eating her from within. On the conscious level, the fetus can be perceived as a promise for the future; or, conversely, it creates apprehension as a drain on the mother's strength. Between these two poles we see a variety of attitudes and reactions toward pregnancy and motherhood.

The mother often feels at one with the growing fetus; both are secure and surrounded with protection. Obscure, dreamlike, mystical sensations and imaginings of dissolving the boundaries between herself and the world, or of fusing pleasurably with others, reaching back to the original closeness with her own mother, are stirred up by the "uncanny" experience of having the baby as part of herself. This intimate identification underlies many of the questions which prospective mothers discuss and bring to physicians and nurses, or which find their answers in old wives' tales: "If I think good thoughts and listen to beautiful music during pregnancy, will my child be artistic?" Other women still believe that if they have heartburn, this means that the baby's hair is growing; or if they laugh at a cripple, the baby will be deformed. The morning nausea and, at times, excessive salivation of early pregnancy, the strange food cravings and increased appetite may unconsciously reactivate the most common childhood misconception about pregnancy. Namely, that is a digestive process: father gives mother something by mouth, a pill, a special food, or even a kiss, and then the baby grows inside of her. This theory, which was once conscious, is often operative in cases of excessive, pathological nausea and vomiting based upon an unconscious wish to be rid of the pregnancy—as if the baby were swimming about in the mother's stomach and could be regurgitated.

Perhaps the most familiar irrational concerns in pregnancy center about the sense of guilt. Any unresolved feelings that sex is forbidden or indecent, especially those connected with the oedipal conflict—involving the coveted and at the same time frightening fulfillment of the competitive wish to be the woman in mother's place and to have the children—can lead to this guilt. It may appear as embarrassment over the visible signs of pregnancy, expressing the concern that they reveal one's sexual activity to people—an attitude that frequently results in the well-known delay in seeking prenatal care. Hazards of losing the fetus, of bearing a malformed baby, or of dying during the delivery, however remote the chance of their occurring, are experienced as impending punishment for these actual or fantasied misdeeds. In folk tales and superstitions these dangers are represented as arising from the malicious envy of other women—from wicked witches and possessors of the evil eye.

We are already familiar with the phenomenon of a developmental crisis in puberty where somatic changes and new, intensified libidinal and adjustive tasks confront the individual, lead to the revival of unsettled conflicts, and loosen incomplete solutions of the past. We have to consider the psychological peculiarities of pregnancy from the same viewpoint. In both adolescence and pregnancy the equilibrium of the personality is temporarily upset and the resulting disturbance creates the picture of a far more serious disintegration than need actually ensue. In both instances the outcome of the crisis is of the greatest significance for the mastery of the developmental phase that follows: of adulthood after puberty, of motherhood succeeding pregnancy, and, as we shall see later, that of healthy aging upon solution of the climacteric crisis. However, not all the developmental crises lead to such harmonious stabilization; at times, they may mark the beginning of serious mental and emotional disturbances. It is well known to clinicians that neurotic or even psychotic illnesses may have their onset in adolescence, pregnancy, or menopause.

Although the fact of "having a baby" is often perceived as a full compensation for all of the "blood and thunder," as one patient called the female biology, it is, of course, not necessarily synonymous with achieving full emotional motherhood. Usually a woman must solve some major problems from the past in order to achieve a true maturational move toward motherhood. These pertain first of all to certain attitudes toward her own mother, which in most young women are found as vestiges of their childhood conflicts. Among these are a helpless dependency, as if the woman were still a little girl in need of protection and sustenance from mother, or a continuation of warfare with mother, a rebellion which started in early adolescence, so that anything mother stands for has to be fought bitterly; or an overobedient submissiveness as a way of warding off her early, hostile impulses against mother as a rival. All of these have to give way to a feeling of strength and equality. She is no longer just her mother's child, but must feel free to become the mother of her own baby, without either anxiously looking toward her parent for permission and sustenance or using her new role as a demonstration to prove how much better she can be than her mother.

A similar shift has to take place in her attachment to her father. The childhood ties have to be loosened so that her husband can now in his own right represent for her the image of the mature, responsible male, the father of her child and provider for her family. This necessarily involves the resolution of her childhood inhibitions, fears, and guilt concerning her sexual feelings and experiences; and a full acceptance of her feminine role and function, undisturbed by infantile jealousy and competition with the little boys of her earlier years and the big boys and men as she grew up. Successful psychological growth during pregnancy will lead to diminution or resolution of these conflicts.

As we have mentioned previously, the mother makes her first direct acquaintance with her child when she perceives its movements in the second trimester. We believe that realization and acceptance of her new function and role in the family and the wider social group, as an adult woman and mother, begin at this time.

This changing concept of herself was once expressed in the simplest yet most poignant form by a young primigravida, an intelligent college graduate, not a naïve or unsophisticated woman, who attended one of the group therapy sessions in our Prenatal Clinic. She arrived late when all of the expectant mothers and some of their husbands were already involved in a discussion about their coming babies. Without any introduction she cut into the sentence just spoken by one of the members and, still on her way to her chair, she said with a breathless excitement, "I was quite excited last night, quite anxious! It suddenly struck me that I won't be Jeanie much longer, but mother forever and ever after!" Then she added with intense emotion that she had always tried to be away from home and independent of her own mother and that she had many quarrels with her over it. But as she thought about herself, the baby, and her mother last night, she became aware all at once that her mother had not been like any other person for her but somebody unique. Whenever something happened to her, she must have thought first of all of running to her mother—though she did not do it. Now she clearly felt how she will be this person all by herself for a child, her own baby. And Jeanie, the girl she had been throughout from the time when she was little until now, would exist no longer. Everybody in the room looked at her and listened in rapt silence.

What happened to Jeanie was the beginning shift from the psychological position of a single, self-contained, independent individual with little awareness of the significance of a mother's relation to her child, to the position of a mother who carries her baby within herself and who will always have a special relationship to him. She will have to establish and will have to combine two opposite feelings toward him. On the one hand, he will be experienced as an independent person in his own right, and yet, on the other hand, he will always remain an extension of herself whom she does not want to lose to the world.

The mother's emerging appreciation of the new baby as a reality and of her future role of motherhood, shown with all the drama of sudden insight by Jeanie, marks the start of a long process of psychological differentiation in the mother that will accompany the growth of independence in her child. With childbirth and the actual physical separation many women are aware of feelings of loss and mild grief, the post-partum blues, along with the relief, relaxation, pride, and pleasure. In some cases of severe psychological postpartum disturbances, we may find that the central issue is the necessity to part from the baby, as if a most vital and essential part of herself had to be given up. In other women, the fact of separation may lead to denial, causing these mothers to attempt in various ways to control the entire lives of their children.

During the first period of infancy the psychological separation is normally only rudimentary, and closeness between mother and infant is paramount. In our discussion of the oral period of development we emphasized the indispensability for the young child of a constant, consistently and warmly gratifying mothering person. The case of Paul (Lecture 3), the foundling boy who had been reared in an institutional environment that was too cold and too rigid for him, was a striking example of the consequences of insufficient maternal care. The importance of the mother as the first object for the baby's future mental health was underscored not only by direct observations of the impact of maternal deprivation but also in studies of the development and course of juvenile delinquency, adult character disorders, psychosomatic illnesses, borderline states, and psychoses. At the same time the subject was taken up in contemporary literature, sometimes with considerable indignation, sarcasm, and despair: most marital difficulties, failures in adjustment and achievement, and even the spiritual deficiencies of a mass culture were attributed to "Mom," her apron strings, and silver cord.

Here, certain considerations would weigh against these sweeping conclusions. Our understanding of the long and complex course of individual development cautions against giving exclusive emphasis to any one factor as a universal cause of psychopathology. We know that strong and active mothers in combination with gentle, but ineffective fathers who seem to abdicate their rights as head of the family complicate the development of their children considerably. Moreover, "Mom" and "Daddy" must be understood in the light of the history of the specific, changing family conditions of American life.[2] At the same time this undesirable extremism must not induce us to overlook something important: that emotional difficulties in the mother lead to chronic malformation of the earliest mother-child relationship that will inevitably result in disturbances—independent of any cultural configurations.

If the mother's own persistent unconscious childhood impulses or the difficulties of her early development have not been sufficiently overcome, they will find their way into her attitude toward her child's normal functions and needs, that is, they will affect her management of the feeding situation, the child's active aggressiveness, his demandingness, the toilet training, masturbation, as well as many other aspects of his behavior. This may come about by her overreacting to the baby's tendencies, either by her endeavoring to suppress them rigidly, or disregarding them, or through her being

[2] It is our impression that in a cultural environment where, through historical and social conditions, the functions of the mother and the father are not sufficiently separated, a certain confusion of roles may result for the child. Taking the development of the boy as an illustration, we find in the optimum situation that the mother is the nurturing emotional object while the father is the idealized model for masculinity who enforces behavioral standards. In a constellation where mother is unavoidably the first erotic object for the little boy, but at the same time has to take over too much of the restraining and enforcing position, the boy finds both attraction and the threat of punishment combined in this one figure. This leads ever so often to a disturbed attitude toward women, both in childhood and later on, in which infantile fears overshadow feelings of love; the relationship to a woman is then shot through and dominated by ideas of her punitive power and the danger involved in being close to her—a composite of what is usually distributed in childhood between father and mother (G. L. Bibring, 1953). Erik H. Erikson (1950) has discussed "mom" in relation to the early history of the United States. He stresses the influence of the Western frontier and the Puritan tradition upon the role of women and upon child rearing.

inconsistent. Whatever her specific difficulty, it will interfere with her adequate handling of these situations and lead to disturbance in these functions in the child. We have already examined instances in which this occurred: for example, Mrs. C., the mother whose earlier phobia of tuberculosis reappeared as an irrational, "overprotective" concern that her first baby might contract that disease if the infant did not eat properly, with the outcome of a feeding difficulty (Lecture 3). And as a form of disregarding important functions in the child, we described the case of the young professional woman, Mrs. E., whose overindulgent neglect to toilet train her son led to his maladjustment and destructive behavior at nursery school (Lecture 4).

The profound emotional changes that occur in pregnancy may not only influence its course but also affect the future relationship of the mother and child. For this reason we believe that good prenatal management includes an awareness on the part of the physician of the mother's special need for preventive psychological care and understanding. As in pediatrics or in the treatment of illness in young adolescents, the physician should be prepared to pay attention to his patient's emotional equilibrium. In our modern society, it is often the responsibility of the prenatal team of obstetrician, nurse, and social worker to help the prospective mother to feel secure, a task they can achieve on the basis of understanding the woman's particular problems and the difficulties arising from the experience of pregnancy.

In former days pregnancy, childbirth, and the transition to a new social role were explicitly, even ceremonially, recognized by the community. Midwives and the old women of the family and clan were in attendance and exercised a protective, ritualistic function to safeguard the pregnancy. Among more primitive groups taboos and religious laws were observed in order to ease labor pains and to ward off jealous and malignant spirits. The woman who attained motherhood also advanced in status within the community along traditionally established and fixed lines.

Today both the superstitions, fears, and the support of the communtiy have receded. Many young couples live in comparative isolation at a distance from their parents and relatives, and witchcraft has been replaced by effective modern medicine. Paradoxically, however, though advances in obstetrical and neonatal care have made childbirth safe and relatively painless, it often seems as though the old prejudices have merely been replaced by the opposite myth: namely, that pregnancy is invariably a beautiful, blissful state unsullied by inner conflicts. Despite medical progress, less attention is paid to the unchanged, deeper anxieties and inner psychological processes of adjustment in pregnancy. An immigrant mother speaking to a visiting nurse expressed a direct, spontaneous awareness of these needs within her when she said that if it were possible, she would like to be delivered at home, near her family: "Where I came from everyone in the village knew about it and wanted to help when you were going to have a baby. Here you go up to that machine on the hill . . . !" —the modern community hospital.

The "normal crisis" of pregnancy usually does not make a strong impression upon us. As a matter of fact, there are women who are inclined to keep all possible disturbances under complete control, presenting to the doctor only the picture of unruffled strength, total command of the situation, and reasonableness. They tend to ask for full information and they read up on everything that pertains to pregnancy and delivery. This phenomenon is almost exclusively restricted to the compulsive character type whose special way of handling anxieties has been described (G. L. Bibring, Dwyer, Huntington, and Valenstein, 1961).

What we see in the average woman is a degree of apprehension and moodiness, a tendency to withdraw from the social environment, irritability, and overdependency, some mild problems around diets, a lack of preparation for the baby, concern about minor physical symptoms, a preoccupation with the development of the fetus, or special tenseness with regard to the delivery. Anxiety is often attached to realistic worry, e.g., about financial problems, and may be expressed through tension symptoms like headaches. Early in pregnancy we may observe an augmented concern with nausea or food cravings. There may be difficulties in accepting the alteration from a youthful type of beauty to a more maternal appearance, and some women react to this by postponing unduly to wear any maternity clothes, others by going to the extreme of neglecting their figures and giving up their interest in being attractive altogether.

An initial bewilderment and doubt about being pregnant, as in the form of "I can't believe that I am actually going to have a baby," may be succeeded by behavior expressing the woman's rejection of the pregnant state by excessively increasing her physical activities or failing to adhere to diets and to keep her regular prenatal appointments. Any actual physical problem can become the focus of profound anxiety. Concern about the normality of the baby may center upon fetal activity (too much or too little), Rh factor, colds or other infections, apprehension about strangulation by the umbilical cord, and especially fears that the baby may be deformed. Fears of bleeding, pain, and bodily damage or of receiving anesthesia are always associated with impending childbirth.

When crisis reactions are intense and persistent despite reasonable attention to them, we are alerted to possible psychopathology. As can be expected, pre-existing neurotic tendencies and marital problems are often intensified in pregnancy, and the memories of previous, relevant, traumatic experiences, such as miscarriages and stillbirths, may again become sources of tension. We anticipate and often find emotional disturbance when the pregnancy is unwanted or when the prospective mother appears specially vulnerable, as indicated by a history of mental illness, immaturity, limited intelligence, or the recent loss of a protective key figure. Similarly we are prepared to offer support when she faces unusual stress like Caesarean section, pregnancy late in the childbearing period, multiple births, or medical conditions such as toxemia, diabetes, heart disease, hyperthyroidism, epilepsy, etc. With the great variety of elements that become stirred up in this situation, there is no single way of describing or dealing with them; but rather, as always in good medical practice, one must carefully consider the individual case of crisis.

The following case in its simplicity may serve as an example of what we call the normal crisis and of the way in which help can be offered to prevent more serious difficulties. Mrs. W., a small, friendly, and attractive, twenty-three-year-old primigravida, was first seen in our Prenatal Clinic during the third month of pregnancy. She exhibited a moderate degree of anxiety and an inclination to become excessively concerned or irritated over relatively minor incidents. She said that she had been frightened by the pelvic examination without exactly knowing why, and then mentioned that her mother had died four years previously of cancer of the uterus. She was concerned with her weight which she regarded as being too low, although objectively it was within the normal range. The patient reported that she had tried to become pregnant for two and a half years. During the past year there had been some irregularity of her menstrual periods which had been interpreted as a possible miscarriage. After asking if it was all right for her to continue to enjoy bowling, she went on to tell about a friend of hers who was a medical student. She had gone through some of his textbooks and had seen pictures of fetal monstrosities. Afterward he had talked to her about her pregnancy, and she felt that she had gained some reassurance that it would turn out well.

In a subsequent interview during her regular prenatal visit, she began by asking a question about constipation which she had noticed recently. Then she spoke of an aunt who took cathartics and had had a hysterectomy two years previously. This again led to the thought of her mother's illness and now she told of her parents having been divorced when she was very small and of her having been placed in a foster home for several years. The patient had come to resemble her mother in being a hard-working person, and, when mother was sick, she had taken care of her. This then led to an extensive discussion of mother's illness.

In talking of sickness Mrs. W. remarked, "I like to know about things before they happen to me." Once she had had an ear puncture, the thought of which scared her very much, and she found it very helpful that the doctor had allowed her to examine the instruments beforehand. Accordingly, it was suggested to her that she might like to visit and become acquainted with the obstetrical floor of the hospital prior to her confinement. When she went to see the rooms and nursery shortly before term, she was very pleased to find it such an attractive place and was excited by the presence of all the babies she saw there.

Behind this young woman's anxiety, her frequent remarks about gynecological exigencies in her family which led to her mother's death and her aunt's hysterectomy, behind her concern about her weight and the normal development of the baby, we could discern the outlines of primitive fantasies. The unconscious idea that stood out most clearly was a fear of the fetus as a growth, a cancer threatening to damage her as the malignancy had consumed her mother. Her prospective motherhood had rekindled memories and feelings about her own mother, with whom she was closely identified. In the past she had had to cope with the losses of her parents following their divorce and her placement in the foster home; her mother's death reinforced this early trauma. One might expect that these experiences had left her with a special need for care during stressful periods. But unfortunately she was actually deprived of attention, as she had no living relatives of her own and her husband's family lived at a distance. She had dealt previously with her anxieties in an active way, working hard and preparing herself in advance for difficult experiences by learning to know about the details of what she must expect. As a result her overall adjustment had been good.

As is characteristic of a person in normal crisis, she responded favorably to careful psychological management. On the basis of her traumatic experiences and her well-established, habitual defense of fighting anxiety by the knowledge of objective facts, we offered her the opportunity to become familiar with the reality of the procedures of delivery and the lying-in period, including, later, the pediatrician's careful instruction in newborn care, to replace her vague but powerful apprehensions. We supported every effort on her part to establish a closer relationship to her husband's family, which led to regular visits by her mother-in-law who periodically stayed for some days with her. Finally, we discussed the objective facts of her mother's illness, which assuaged her superstitious conviction that she might suffer a similar fate, based upon her strong feelings of identification with her mother.

At the beginning of our discussion of pregnancy, we noted the importance for the prospective mother of a well-founded marriage. This general observation often gains special emphasis in our modern society when young couples live at a considerable distance from their parents or other close relatives, as was the case with our patient. Here the husband is truly the main figure to whom the young mother turns with all of her reanimated needs and inner apprehensions. Evidence of this can be seen in the wife's fear that her husband may resent her for directing her attention to the baby, or that he may become absorbed in his love for the child and neglect her. Although the father is naturally less completely involved than the mother in the advent or the care of the child, fatherhood is a most significant emotional experience for a man. It does not comprise a developmental crisis in the same way that pregnancy does, since it lacks the physiological component, but it calls for new adaptations and leads to lasting changes in the father's role within the family. During his wife's pregnancy, and subsequently as a parent, he must initiate a new responsibility and establish a new kind of relationship with his wife and his child.

The coming of children tests the strength of a marriage, calling upon both partners for greater commitment: consolidating their union yet adding some strain to it. In considering or planning a baby, particularly the first one, the husband must face the potential loss of a significant part of his wife's attention and interest. He may be consciously aware of feeling excluded, or his anxiety may become attached to realistic worries about the problems of increased financial obligation and personal responsibility posed by the enlargement of the family. He may respond with feelings of frustration or dissatisfaction to his wife's pregnancy, her greater self-concern, and her turning inward. Their relationship may be affected by changes in her physical appearance, her morning sickness, peculiar food cravings, and increased dependence upon him. Intervals in which their sexual life is interrupted by his wife's condition may add to his sense of being deprived.

On the other hand, he can share her contentment and pleasant anticipation of the child, and her apprehensiveness and impatience at the outcome of the pregnancy, gaining satisfaction in fulfilling her needs for care and understanding and his own needs for being the provider and protector. In a mitigated form many of the psychological responses found in mothers apply to the father as well. For him, his wife's pregnancy is public evidence of their sexual activity and his potency. The baby might represent a triumph and reward that invites the magically threatening envy of others and thus be a reminder of childhood anxieties. Or the child may be feared as a rival for the love of the woman, as were his siblings who vied with him for mother's attention.

The husband's deeper involvement in his wife's pregnancy was acknowledged by primitive societies in the wide-spread custom of couvade. In this rite the husband takes to bed before or during the time of his wife's labor; he may refrain from taking food, may groan with mock pains of childbirth, and receive attention shown to women at the time of confinement. The practice is thought to testify to the bond of blood and belonging between the father and the child. We can see that couvade is based upon sympathetic magic. For example, some American Indians explain it as a way of protecting against the danger that might later face the child if the father were to engage in a hazardous task at this time of birth. Moreover, they believe that if the father were careless in his diet, then the child would inherit the bad qualities of the animals the father had eaten.

Turning back to our own enlightened and less expressive epoch, when ceremonial observance of fatherhood is often limited to handing out cigars and attending the baptism or circumcision, we have noted that a surprising number of fathers-to-be reacted in an unexpected way: during their wives' pregnancies these young husbands ever so often would "lose" their jobs or get sick, spend significant periods around the home, and behave as if they themselves needed all the attention of their wives, instead of permitting the wife to concentrate upon herself and the child within her (G. L. Bibring, 1959; G. L. Bibring, Dwyer, Huntington, and Valenstein, 1961; and a full presentation of this study in preparation).

The achievement of fatherhood normally represents a decisive step in the attainment of the man's predominant masculine position, equal to that of his own father. But the actual relationship with the child develops more slowly and with less intensity than in the case of the mother. Her life centers around the infant, while for the father, his career is the focus of activity. In addition to the custom in our culture that fathers do not take over the regular care of little babies, a man is inclined to ward off his own childhood impulses that are aroused by the infant's helpless dependence, nursing, weaning, teething, and soiling, by avoiding attending to the baby. For a variety of reasons then, some originating in the mother as well as in the child, the father does not become significantly involved with his offspring until the youngster enters the early genital phase of development. This is by and large true even though fathers enjoy their very small children, and like to play and romp with them. To the child, especially the boy in the early genital phase, father will ideally assume the role of a kind and loving, but firm, regulating, and limit-setting figure. Increasingly and particularly in adolescence, he serves as a model for the skills and the will to face and to cope with the environment. And to his daughter, he represents the first male object for the little girl.

When the father forsakes this role or, at the other extreme, overplays it in the form of paternal depotism toward his son or seductiveness toward his daughter, this may precipitate disturbances in the children, especially in adolescence when the children have to free themselves from the infantile aspects of their relationship to their parents and have to attain a feeling of strength and independence, and make their own choice of occupation and marriage. It results in the familiar intensification of the struggles between the generations.

The father may insist, as if his son were above all an extension of himself, that his son continue successfully his own strivings in his business or profession and accomplish all that he himself could not achieve; or he might react to his son as a competitor whose growing maturity and strength threaten his own sense of adequacy. He may jealously fail to encourage his daughter's feminine interest in boys or insist that she must only marry a man no less capable or successful than himself. This feeling that the son and daughter should carry on as part of himself—thus assuring his immortality—appears frequently in the father's overconcern with his children's standards. It is surprising how often fathers caught up in these issues disregard their rational judgment concerning whether their aims are appropriate in terms of the children's individual needs, abilities, interests, desires, and maturity. Once before, in discussing adolescence, we noted that these struggles often involve two individuals in crisis, the young person and the middle-aged parent. Our understanding of these conflicts will be increased by an examination of the normal developmental crisis of aging.

Adaptation and its failures in adult life have been discussed not only in this chapter and the preceding one, but earlier as we projected the consequences of the child's developmental experiences into adulthood, as far as they determine personality functioning and the manner of meeting traumatic events, especially physical illnesses. A new direction enters in the period of aging, when the emphasis is upon restriction of the scope of life and renunciation of gratifying activities, roles, and ambitions, leading to important problems which are often brought to the physician.

12

Aging and Old Age

"An aged man is but a paltry thing,
A tattered coat upon a stick, unless
Soul clap its hands and sing, and louder sing
For every tatter in its mortal dress."
William Butler Yeats

It is both a tribute and a challenge to modern medicine that
so many people now live to old age. With advances in protecting and sustaining life and health, there have come,
increasingly, the pressing and often unique problems of illness
in the elderly—giving special impetus to our interest in the
period of aging. This last stage of life is mainly the resultant
of ongoing biological processes which include progressive
cellular changes, the deterioration of irreplaceable bodily
structures and functions, and the accumulation of imperfectly
repaired injuries (Comfort, 1956). These phenomena bring
about an alteration in the behavior of the organism which
leads to decreased adaptability and prepares the way to death.
The senile processes of decline vary in time of manifestation,
rate, and regularity. Illustrating this: the rate of growth of
tissues in ratio to their size diminishes from birth; muscular
strength may decrease after the age of twenty-five or thirty

years; the lessening of the power of visual accommodation has been detected from ten years of age and increases more abruptly as "presbyopia" at age forty-five; an artery may "harden" imperceptibly over decades, perhaps leading to a sudden occlusion. Among the manifold physical changes of senescence involving all bodily systems, some affect different individuals more than others, be it the changes in appearance, strength, endurance, eating and elimination, sexual functioning, vision and hearing, or intellectual powers and reaction speed.

Added to these organic impairments are important personal, socioeconomic, and cultural stresses. With advancing years the time passes for having children and for the realization of dreams of achievement. Sooner or later all elderly persons are grieved and isolated by the deaths of their spouses, other members of their family, and close friends. Children may move away. Eventually regulations of our society or the decline in productivity or a shift in motivation lead to retirement from work. The resulting financial decrease is accompanied by loss of social role and status in the family and community, and of the feeling of usefulness that came from their activities and the daily give-and-take with co-workers.

The self-respect of the older person may be further attenuated by the responses of a culture that glorifies youth and restless achievement, with a prevalence of popular prejudices that are derogatory to the elderly, like the stereotyped view of old age as a period of stagnation and inexorable senile decline. However, despite the influence of senescence and social pressures, not all of the events associated with aging represent loss of function, and the psychological and social changes of later life include adjustive efforts and solutions of problems. With regard to this we shall offer the hypothesis that aging does not denote exclusively a stage of deterioration, but rather there is reason to consider it as a developmental phase, comparable to other periods like adolescence, that includes specific biological and social elements and characteristic situations of crisis to which the individual must adapt (H. Deutsch, 1944-1945; Benedek, 1950).

The principal critical events of this period include the climacterium, the termination of useful employment, physical illnesses, and personal losses. All of these may represent pitfalls for the mental health of the individual, but equally the solution and mastery of the problems that they entail promise growth of personality and important new life experiences. We shall begin with those aspects which represent disruptive threats in order to comprehend and to highlight the normal or optimum achievement.

The biologically determined ending of the reproductive period in women from about forty-five years on is a comparatively more taxing event than the corresponding, less conspicuous, and more gradual decline of men's virile strength. The central feature of the female climacterium is the diminution and eventual cessation of ovarian functioning. Direct physical consequences include irregularity and then termination of menstruation, ending of the capacity to bear children, disturbance of the functioning of other endocrine organs, and atrophy of the genitals. The loss of youthful appearance and feminine beauty is an important feature of aging at this time. Physiological reactions may be prominent, particularly early in the climacterium, and include the well-known vasomotor phenomena of hot flashes, perspiring, dizziness, and headaches. The mothering function as a biological experience and a vital role in the family no longer can serve as a source of full gratification with the end of the ability to have babies and the increasing independence of the growing children. A surge of activity is common, especially at the beginning of the climacterium, as a reflection of both the disturbance of the woman's psychological equilibrium between impulses and inner control—under the impact of emotional and physiological tensions—and of her endeavor to cope with this imbalance. Dormant interests from early adolescence may reappear, such as in artistic pursuits or a late career. Psychological conflicts with resultant neurotic symptoms can be revived. The desire for experiences before it is too late may be expressed in increased sexual activity or the attempt to have another child.

While men are vulnerable in their self-esteem to the diminution of libido and physical power, and show analogous compensatory efforts, they often feel hit much harder by retirement from employment. A man's work achievements frequently symbolize indirectly his contribution as a male. Retirement may literally leave him without any essential occupation, whereas a woman who gives up her job can continue quite appropriately as a homemaker. However, for both men and women it leads to a disruption of personal contacts, a loss of the work group with whom ties have been established through many years, and consequently to some isolation. Beyond this, in our culture, as much as we may complain about our tasks, work fulfills an important function in channeling inner tensions and drives toward socially valued goals and achievements; we call this process sublimation, i.e., "objectionable" impulses like aggression or greed or self-centeredness, when sublimated, may take the form of independence, ambition, leadership, etc., in the service of professional and social strivings. To close this valuable outlet can lead to tensions, increased self-criticism, and depression.

Another impressive factor is the prevalence of physical illnesses in older people. Sicknesses not only occur with greater frequency and multiplicity in the elderly than in younger persons, but they are more often life-threatening, tend to require longer convalescence, and are likely to become chronic or disabling. Acute episodes of disease may be accompanied by mental confusion or delirium, especially in aging patients with diminished functional reserve of vital organs or systems, including those with sensory impairments and the small group who have organic brain disorders. Being hospitalized may itself contribute significantly to their disorientation: many older persons, like young children, react anxiously to the separation from their homes and families; they may be bewildered and frightened by new surroundings, by meeting strange people, and by unfamiliar diagnostic and treatment procedures—especially the use of needles and other instruments; older patients often find it hard to accept the interruption of comforting daily routines and the imposition of different ones. A severe sickness may be a truly traumatic experience, overburdening the individual with anxiety. Recurrent or chronic disease prolongs his actual dependence upon others and wears down his strong defenses against infantile needs. All of this helps us to understand the common preoccupation of many older persons with their physical state, and the importance to them of physicians and treatments.

Among the most drastic assaults upon the psychic stability of the older individual are the unavoidable losses of friends and relatives which render him increasingly lonely. Each death of an emotionally highly valued person induces painful sadness and shock at its finality, even when it has been expected and, so to speak, mourned in advance. A flood of memories brings home the deprivation and these recur with feelings of grief perhaps during several years. Although this intense preoccupation usually gives way to a resigned acceptance of the reality, the consequences of the event remain as the loss of a spouse, a friend and companion, a benefactor or someone to take care of and contend with. The older individual, in contrast to the young one, has less opportunity and time and energy to invest in new relationships and activities which could replace, to some extent, what he has lost.

What are the assets of the elderly which they can bring to the task of meeting these stressful changes? We know that under favorable circumstances the confrontation with these oppressing experiences may lead to adjustment, achievements characteristic for the healthy, aging person, and further maturation or ripening of the personality. Old age when appraised objectively holds, by the very same token of its emotional disentanglement and cooling off, and by the lifting of the heavy burden of modern life with its demanding work conditions and pressing responsibilities, a freedom of choice which may never have existed before. The receding sexual drive does not necessarily lead to intense anxiety, nor does retirement objectively represent demotion and abandonment; the individual with strength of personality and resilience can accept and integrate certain limiting and disabling physical conditions without an inner breakdown. Although all these events are taxing, especially the accumulation of losses of beloved people, which is the most serious challenge to a person's inner resources, they lie within the area of human adaptability. They can be surmounted by the individual who has experienced a measure of gratification and success in his life, who has been resilient in the face of assaults upon his self-esteem, and whose superego has remained tolerant and flexible, permitting modification in the standards of his more active years.

As far as his drives are concerned, when the pressure to gain objects and achievements diminishes, there is an inclination toward needs and satisfactions of earlier years which were always present but played a minor role. There is usually an increase of appreciation of simpler pleasures, like physical comforts and food, and subtle gratification of an aesthetic and intellectual nature. There is a re-emergence of old interests in manual skills, hobbies, painting, literature, nature, contemplation, or leisure, which had to be brushed aside as nonessential compared with the vital tasks of adult life. As regards the social contribution that may be made in this late period: this is an area where many errors and biased judgments and lack of objective knowledge confuse the issue. We know that there are marked differences of opinion among the varied cultures.

In many primitive societies the vigorous individuals who survive into old age have been awarded distinction and prestige (Simmons, 1946). To the oldest is ascribed the highest power, even superhuman ability, and the most immense knowledge. Hence they are revered as magicians, priests, seers, and healers. They rank high within the family circle, and their age is often an asset in qualifying for community leadership as administrators, judges, and lawmakers. They are appreciated as possessors of special skills like crafts and art, or leaders in games and songs and dances, and as storytellers and tribal historians. Also, in highly developed, stabilized cultures with strong family ties, with religious and philosophical systems which value meditation, tranquility, tolerance, and experience, and which do not overidealize ambition, hyperactivity, and worldly achievements, the old person by far surpasses the younger one in esteem and in stature as the counselor and arbiter (Chandler, 1949).

In the tradition of the American society, youth and strength and the ability to innovate, to change with the new and to dare and venture, are the most admired qualities. We have our older justices and senior statesmen, but it is more the rule that, although the conservative, slow-moving, and reminiscing aged person may be tolerated and treated kindly, he has little or no significant public function or value. This in turn fosters the general misconception that he is intellectually not quite competent.

If we now distinguish carefully between the organically damaged central nervous system, which is one of the pathologies of aging, and the healthy system, the question arises: what are the characteristic changes in the normal older person? There are studies which lead to the following interesting conclusion: there is a slowing down of perceptual processes and, therefore, the older person is less able to scan incoming stimuli and evaluate them as quickly as the younger one; notably, after fifty years of age, there is a prolongation of the time spent in resting or recovering between mental or physical actions that call for accurate perception and adjustment to changing stimuli; this decline is not uniform or specifically predictable (Lorge, 1939). However, though the responses are slower, they are not less discriminating than in the younger individual. Furthermore, the normal seventy-year-old scores better than the twenty-five- and thirty-five-year-old in verbal intelligence, that is, in the amount of organized, stored information. The Chinese acknowledged this, expressing it in their saying: "If you wish to succeed, consult three old people." In contrast to performance in the laboratory, under real life conditions older workers organize their tasks well, have fewer accidents and less breakage, and need less supervision, thus proving as effective as the younger ones (Welford, 1959). Furthermore, while it appears that major innovations and discoveries tend to be made before middle age, creative productivity often continues into the very late years.

The qualities of older individuals that we have touched upon so far—their relative freedom from instinctual duress, their opportunity and capacity to reflect and to enjoy the incidents of daily life, and their accumulated experiences and knowledge and broader understanding of life—are seen most clearly as assets in those areas of activity where detachment, perspective, the ability to represent and interpret civilized standards and ideals, aesthetic appreciation and pleasure in the course of events count the most—as among teachers, judges, artists, clinicians, and craftsmen. To these personal resources we may add the following: for many, a wealth of possessions remains from the past—mementos, loyalties, continued friendships, family ties, etc.; attachments to the younger generation are established—a love free from the worries and conflicts of control and rivalry and ambition encountered in raising and being responsible for one's own children; they return to their memories (which are as real as events) with new understanding; and especially for those with physical health, there is abiding vigor, independence, and a sense of time ahead to accomplish things.

When individuals are unable to solve the tasks of aging successfully, we find certain typical disturbances. In the most frequent case the varied events which tax the older person's self-respect may lead predominantly to depressive symptoms: he feels sad and worn out and is preoccupied with disappointments and personal losses; he rejects and despises himself, feeling that he is no good, or worse that he has never been any good, has no right to go on, does not even want to live, that nobody cares for him and he deserves nothing better. When this frame of mind is most marked and is coupled with the ability and tendency to take action, suicide becomes a serious danger.

The depressive syndrome usually includes a number of other elements, and, as with the lowering of self-esteem, they may range in intensity from mild to most severe. The characteristic mood of sadness may deepen to despondent hopelessness. A prevailing state of helplessness, where the patient is unable to concentrate or accomplish anything, may reach the proportion of a paralyzed stupor. The effort to struggle against self-hatred and feelings of despair and weakness sometimes is reflected in a search for substitute comfort and gratification, like extravagant spending, overeating, and drinking, as if to fill this unbearable void and relieve tension.

With it go, characteristically, infinite pleas and demands for help from others. The severely depressed person is slowed down in his thinking and actions, does not want to eat, loses weight, and is exhausted, yet cannot sleep or recover his strength. It is not uncommon for a depressed patient to describe to his physician only his somatic symptoms, like indigestion, weight loss, constipation, insomnia, and fatigue, so that the background of self-devaluation and sadness is not immediately apparent. In the extreme form of a psychosis, the patient may believe irrationally that his body has been destroyed by illness. Many who are prone to depression in late life have had similar reactions earlier in life. Other indications of this vulnerability include: strong dependent needs; difficulty in controlling impulses—especially of rage; a great discrepancy between rigidly maintained ideals, standards, and ambitions on the one hand, and abilities and opportunities for achievement on the other; and an exaggerated emphasis upon physical excellence, as in some virile men and beauty queens whose self-respect leans heavily upon preserving their youthful strength and attractiveness.

There is another pathological reaction which seems so very different from depression in its symptomatology but may be based upon similar deep problems. If a person can no longer cope with the pressure of a mounting conflict, he may switch the scene of this battle from within himself to the outside world. What started out as a harsh, self-condemning judgment is projected onto people in his environment, by whom he then feels persecuted and viciously criticized; he no longer censures his own shortcomings, but instead resentfully reads the criticism into the behavior of others; he does not attack himself for his failings, but rather believes that other people threaten and assail him, ridicule and reject him, and take advantage of him.

This way of dealing with intolerable self-reproaches, which we call the psychological defense of paranoid projection, had occurred in a sixty-five-year-old man, who was seen in consultation. Mr. Z. had suddenly developed paranoid ideas after a serious traumatic operation—the amputation of his leg because of vascular disease. These ideas centered around the unshakable, irrational conviction that his sixty-year-old wife, with whom he had lived in a most harmonious marriage, wanted to get rid of him and was having an illicit affair with the young superintendent of the apartment house where they resided. We understand this as a projection of his own desperate feelings that his very lovable and still attractive wife could not possibly tolerate such a mutilated and disabled husband, and was bound to find this young man much more desirable.

Paranoid reactions that appear in response to illnesses or other stresses frequently represent an intensification of long-standing personality traits of suspiciousness, guardedness (against being "treacherously stabbed in the back"), and oversensitivity to actual or fancied slights and rebuffs—which may be coupled with a self-righteous, querulous tendency to "hit back" against such magnified or imagined "attacks." While this reinforcement of personality traits is relatively more common in the aging, it is also found in younger persons.

We can discern the prototype of the mechanism of projection in the reactions of very young children. The childhood slogan of "I didn't do it—they did it," in trying to avoid facing one's misdemeanors. The youngster who bumps into the table blames "the bad table" rather than his own clumsiness, and the child who wants to avoid the discomfort of facing his misdeeds easily convinces himself and insists: "I didn't do it—you did it!" Both exemplify the use of projection in its simplest form, which upon close scrutiny is not restricted to the unsophisticated way children deal with unpleasant experiences. In many adults we discover this primitive way of restoring their self-confidence by habitually finding fault with others whenever they themselves have failed.

Among the many fears, suspicions, and delusions, one group is of special significance for medical management: vague and well-rationalized ideas of being poisoned by medicine or being damaged through diagnostic or operative procedures. The principles of medical management of such patients are illustrated in the following case:

Mrs. Y., a sixty-year-old woman of this type, who was hospitalized for severe congestive heart failure, repeatedly refused medication to the point where her life was endangered. Although it was possible to approach and converse with her on neutral topics without upsetting her, any discussion of her symptoms immediately led to a frantic and bitter outpouring of complaints. She not only lamented her difficulty in breathing and sleeping, and the anguish of leg pains, but she desperately bemoaned her lack of improvement, ascribing it to the supposed inadequacy of her medical care.

Psychiatric consultation was requested because of this irrational attitude which suggested an emotional disturbance. It was apparent that her leading attitude was one of mistrust, as though the pills and injections brought to her by the nurses were poison. By frustrating the efforts of the medical staff she expressed her vengeful, aggressive feelings over her predicament which she blamed on them. When she refused medicines and fought the doctors and nurses, she temporarily shifted from the position of a "persecuted" individual to being the one in command who could punish and persecute others. However, we could observe that her refusal to cooperate, as adamant as it seemed, was not a final one—she would reject medication only to allow it several hours later and if an injection had made her arm "completely numb and paralyzed," she might instead accept a pill—though this would soon set her stomach "on fire."

In view of her attitude of intense distrust and paranoid anxieties, it was planned that no medication would be offered or medical procedure attempted without a preliminary, careful, realistic explanation of its nature and purpose, including its place in the overall strategy of treatment, so that she would not be taken unaware. Whenever possible she was to be cared for by those of the personnel in whom she seemed to have the most confidence. And her refusal was not to be regarded as absolute: if she refused to accept a pill, the nurse was to acknowledge this hesitation, and at the same time was to say that she would return on her next round and hoped that the patient would feel more up to it then.

While it would have been an error to minimize the patient's complaints, especially in view of her oversensitivity, it was essential to avoid the pitfall of agreeing with her exaggerated protests and thus reinforcing them, but it was also important to avoid what might seem an excessive personal involvement lest the patient feel taken in or manipulated.

One of the nurses who was new to the hospital floor

obtained some independent confirmation of the value of these measures. She offered Mrs. Y. her digitalis without any special explanation as she routinely gave it to other patients who have been for some time on a digitalis regimen, not knowing of the patient's characteristic reactions, and she was refused. Later on, she tried to present it again, this time commenting that, after all, the doctor had prescribed it for the patient's heart condition. The patient took the medicine and said, almost grudgingly, "If you had told me in the first place that this was what my doctor had ordered for my heart, I would have taken it right away." Thus, after having been permitted to control the situation and to refuse the medication, the patient could accept an explanation that would have been immediately obvious to another person: namely, that she had been given a proper, helpful medication. As her physical condition now began to respond she became progressively less quarrelsome and more rationally cooperative.

There is another serious disturbance which is repeatedly seen in the aging. As a result of the distressing senescent changes in the body, especially loss of attractiveness and strength, and as a consequence of physical illnesses and pain, in combination with social isolation and lack of meaningful involvement with others, the individual tends to concentrate with increasing concern upon his own body. Such a patient's preoccupation with fearful ideas of having dangerous illnesses cannot be influenced easily by rational means, and he generally shows little response to attempts at reassurance. Every doctor is familiar with the hypochondriasis of this age group. Older persons who feel unloved or rejected often utilize these symptoms secondarily as an appeal for the concern and attention of their families, neighbors, or doctors.

Completing our overview of the pathology of the aging we find the picture of mental senility in a small proportion of the elderly. This reaction is based upon organic pathology of the central nervous system, but it also involves defensive responses to the anxiety aroused by the individual's awareness of deficits and losses. Foremost among its manifestations are symptoms indicating the impairment of intellectual functions, especially memory, orientation, and social judgment. The recall of recent events declines first and most severely, while memory for the past is affected more gradually. In cases of severe dementia (or in delirium) there is disorientation first to time and then to place, and in the most extreme form not even familiar persons are recognized. The poor judgment of the senile person may appear as an apparent lack of awareness or concern with the impression that he makes upon others, carelessness to the point of endangering himself, as in traffic accidents, and credulousness of the sort that makes some of these elderly people the victims of confidence rackets. The senile patient may laugh and cry easily to the extent of appearing shallow or silly. The characteristic underlying brain damage is diffuse, but it may also be localized and result in paralyses and aphasias. Senility is frequently accompanied by an accentuation of personality traits that is even more marked than the normal deepening of the lines of character that accompanies aging.

The senile patient may attempt to compensate for his memory defect, intellectual slowness, and difficulty in making judgments by becoming garrulous and by confabulating; he shows irritability and oversensitivity if he is questioned. His actual state of helplessness may engender the effort to gain sympathy by ingratiating himself or displaying bravery, an attempt to coax or force care by beseeching, nagging, or coercing others, or a show of defiance to reassure himself of his own strength. Sometimes excessive sexual activity or even sexual indecency may be observed, representing an effort to deny the loss of attractiveness or potency. Defensive measures of withdrawal or turning to more childlike forms of behavior may begin with a lessening of ambition and a dislike of change, and lead to increasing self-absorption, self-reminiscence, taking extensive time with routine, repetitive chores, preoccupation with food and bowels, hoarding of worthless objects, loss of consideration and affection for others, and even to complete isolation and alienation.

Sometimes we see elderly patients who present a picture suggestive of mental deterioration not on the basis of senility, but because their depression or anxiety or hypochondriacal preoccupation interferes with their basically normal intellectual processes. We have already referred to another very alarming phenomenon often seen during illnesses, which likewise may lead to the conviction that mental deterioration is more widely distributed than is objectively the case. This is the rather common picture of acute confusion and agitation with which many older people react to hospitalization and toxic conditions. Pathological as this disturbance certainly is, the dramatic symptoms of clouded consciousness, fluctuating disorientation, memory loss, and panic, often accompanied by sensory illusions and hallucinations, are disproportionately more marked than the degree of any underlying chronic or irreversible brain disorder.

A major reason for this occurrence probably lies in the special changes which lead to slowing down of the evaluation of and responses to perceptions. This person who is in an increased state of tension due to anxiety connected with his illness and to the uncertainty of what will happen to him in the hospital (like any other patient), but also due to his separation anxiety at having to leave behind the few remaining protective figures and objects of his small world (like the child), finds it hard to organize his perceptions of stimuli and to react usefully within the optimum time to the different but appropriate hospital environment. Confusion states are more ominous from the standpoint of physical disease than as indicators of psychiatric prognosis since they often appear as a terminal manifestation. Reversal of the toxic condition and correct psychological management bring about an often remarkable restoration of mental proficiency.

Mildly senile patients who are not depressed, excessively

anxious, suspicious or confused, usually need no special additional care during illnesses, while the severely senile or demented require protective supervision. For all patients, but particularly young children and the elderly, during episodes of acute discomfort, increased helplessness, and especially of temporary confusion and delirium, it is important to provide an additional, constant, protective figure upon whom the patient can rely, like a special nurse, a dependable family member, or even at times another patient. With this, the confused person also needs careful and unhurried explanations of his surroundings and the ongoing activities. Examinations, procedures, and the number of personnel should be restricted to a minimum in order to keep stimuli at a tolerable level. At night the provision of a small light will help prevent the loss of orienting landmarks. Whenever possible it is best to treat him at home, and in the hospital to permit him to maintain familiar routes, and to keep his personal garments and possessions.

In general the doctor plays a very special role for the aged person who, in his greater isolation, deprived of the variety of meaningful relationships, has an intense need for a central figure who cares for him and who pays attention to his trouble (Kahana, 1967). The older patient has a tendency to bring everything that is important for him to his doctor; and if we want to be of help, we must first of all accept this essential role in the world of the patient and permit and encourage him to make use of us in his way. We give every support which is possible—much more than to the younger person—and we want the patient to feel our concern and our appreciation of him as a person of value and dignity. When he begins to make any appropriate move toward independence, we attempt to support and sustain it in order to counteract the regressive tendency to fall into a passive, childish condition. This is particularly important when illness has weakened the resilience of the patient and threatens to lead to clinging and invalidism. We encourage every such move in the direction of self-reliance, appreciate it as a valued effort, and even use persuasion to this end, but we do not force it. We help in the planning of meaningful and productive activity, occupation of the kind that makes use of the patient's ability without being too taxing and strenuous.

With an old person, as in the case of a very young child, the human environment and especially the family must be taken into the therapeutic process. We cannot help being aware that strong emotional conflicts may be stirred up in the family of an aged parent, as much as these feelings are controlled and denied. Stemming from preceding struggles against the lifelong authority of this now feeble individual, there is frequently a remnant of rebellious resentment in the younger persons, and with this goes a reactive guilt about their hidden efforts to break away, to achieve their own independence, and to overthrow the power of the elders. This underlying impulse, though intensely repressed, now may interfere with a genuine, friendly, sympathetic, and appreciative attitude, and can lead to an overcompensating, sacrificial overdoing of filial duties. Extreme devotion and concern in the children to the point that they do not allow the old parent to do anything on his own can interfere considerably with our plans to help the elderly maintain healthy independence.

This difficulty in the younger generation becomes readily apparent to the observer when they react with almost agitated protests to any suggestion that might lessen the strenuous burden of constant care. The physician may have to make a repeated effort in order to alleviate the children's sense of guilt and fear of self-indulgence, and to commit them to a different kind of obligation toward their parents, namely, to help them regain some self-sufficiency.

There is another element in the tense reaction of children toward their failing parents which may lead to even more open friction followed by self-reproach in the children: families frequently react with marked irritation to parents who become hard of hearing or clumsy, who may stumble or are slow or confused. We can observe how much easier it seems to be for friends or even strangers to tolerate these failings and handle them kindly. This grievance has to do with a deep disappointment in a beloved, idealized, childhood figure who "betrays" the children's former confidence and admiration. This is the price the old ones have to pay for what always had seemed their perfection: after having been set up as a model by the young, now they are "failing" them.

These situations are sometimes further complicated as the old person becomes caught in the rivalries between the children. For example, not infrequently the one who assumes the responsibility for the parents and lives with them unconsciously feels caught between a relationship of mutual dependence and his own wish to be free. On the other hand, the child who does not take direct care of the parents often carries a grievance for not having been chosen as close enough to them. In this characteristic clash of ambivalent feelings, the former may complain that the other children are thoughtless and neglectful, while the latter blames him for being thoughtless and unkind toward the parents.

Like part of the younger generation we as doctors too might find it particularly difficult to respond helpfully to the aged. This is reflected in the many half-humorous, half-despairing references to old complainers or "crocks." There is not only an awakening of our guilt or disappointment, but we may be distressed by the physical signs of aging which remind us, disconcertingly, of our own future fate. When we try to treat the elderly, we may be troubled by special difficulties in communication. They often speak unclearly, put us off with circumstantial details, exclude us with laconic answers or stubborn, sullen, or taciturn silence, or bombard us with shifting, minor complaints. Worst of all, they frustrate the doctor's therapeutic ambition with their chronic, frequently intractable ailments or terminal conditions—while often, at the same time, turning to us with desperate pleas and magical hopes. And yet here as much as anywhere in medicine a great deal can be accomplished through thoughtful attention to all the details, to symptoms and disturbances, with fruitful gains in mitigating and relieving the distress, thus comforting, preventing premature decline, and adding rewarding months and years to life.

Any consideration of aging, as of the entire course of life, is incomplete without attention to the fact of death, of the individual's consciousness of it, its impact, and the ways in which it is approached. We know that it has different meanings for different individuals. Thoughts of death are avoided or faced in a variety of ways. We see evidence of its ultimate importance for many older persons in their increased interest in religion—in their desire to have a coherent view of life and to pay ceremonial attention to its stages, to gain compensation for their personal losses, to deny the finality of death, and to find some form of explanation of the unknowns in the universe. The way in which death is approached becomes our very serious concern as physicians when we treat someone who suffers from a terminal illness.

From the time that the physician, his patient, or the patient's family suspect the actual fatal nature of the disease, and certainly when this is fully established, a crisis begins for all concerned. From the doctor's viewpoint, this is initially often concentrated in the question of what the patient should or should not be told of his prognosis. The answer will depend not only on what the patient already knows or imagines but foremost on his personality—on his leading conflicts and the nature and effectiveness of his defensive attitudes. The fears aroused in every person by the prospect of dying, which may be extremely intense, take their deeper meaning for the individual from the basic threatening situations of childhood, reaching back to the earliest phases of life.

For the person with strong dependent needs, the imminence of separation from all those to whom he has felt close and upon whom he has relied becomes a threat of being abandoned. This can lead to a state of intense and unyielding despondency which goes far beyond the almost universal depressive reactions that accompany terminal illness. It is manifested in importunate demands for care or cravings for alcohol or medicines, and in desperate struggles against leaving home for urgently required hospitalization. For patients who have lived in the shadow of anxieties due to unsolved mutilation fears, dread of the unknown can take the form of vivid and gruesome fantasies about the destructive changes wrought by diseases and death. This may be expressed through insistent and repetitive questions about the medical findings, the results of tests and X-rays, and the course of treatment. The person who is prone to feelings of guilt over unconscious aggressive impulses may experience the illness as an assault upon him and a punishment, and be preoccupied with thoughts of remorse. People who have set an extreme value upon achievement and activity to assuage their underlying fears of weakness and passivity may concentrate on death as an overpowering force against which there is no recourse. The image of the grave may provoke phobic anxieties of being trapped in a closeness that is both deeply desired and yet has to be warded off. These are only some of the variety of characteristic forms which fear of death can assume in different individuals. Every person has his own concept of dying.

Among all kinds of people, ranging from those who always seek out danger and challenge it directly in a daring, counterphobic way, to persons who have adjusted almost entirely by avoiding and withdrawing from hazards, the protective defense of denying their condition is prominent. Some use denial only as a shield against the greatest emergencies, like the shock of first encountering their sickness in all of its implications, and at times when their symptoms become perceptibly worse. Others rely upon denial constantly, inquiring very little and speaking of their diseases, if they mention them at all, euphemistically as infections or rheumatism. The patient may appear to recognize the nature of his sickness while actually denying its significance and emotional repercussions. A woman who had been operated upon for a malignant tumor of the ovary volunteered with cheerful unconcern that she had cancer. When her understanding of this affliction was gently questioned, she disclosed that she regarded her disease as a very mild one and that she had no conscious notion of what "cancer" meant. Another patient may press eagerly to learn the details of his illness, asking about his prognosis and the results of tests, but one can infer from his confusion or apparent lack of comprehension upon receiving any slightly unfavorable information that he can only bear to hear good news.

Human beings need some sustaining hope for the future in order to avoid despair and depression. However, there is a spectrum of need: at the one extreme are persons, rare as they might be, who approach dying with the same acceptance that they have shown throughout life when meeting the inevitable turning points. They lean upon illusions sparingly, and only at the most desperate junctures. These are often people who have lived their lives fully, have found stable solutions for their childhood anxieties, and have learned to deal with imminent threats and dangers in a realistic and rational way. For them death might be a logical outcome of life and not a crushing trauma. At the other pole are those who require constant reinforcement of their courage with every shred of hopeful possibility.

The question of "how to tell the patient," which is often uppermost in the physician's mind, can be solved only together with the overall important issue of upholding and stabilizing the patient through all the vicissitudes of the final illness. We have to approach the subject cautiously and deliberately, making certain of the diagnosis, and giving the patient some partial and tentative indications which allow him to prepare his defenses and permit us, at the same time, to observe how he reacts to this preliminary information. We listen for indirect clues, whether he speaks of his illness or shuns the topic, in what manner he has used knowledge in any prior sickness. He may disclose whether or not he could discuss his illness with others, or tell us what he thinks in general of how much people should or should not be told; above all, we have an opportunity to discover his personal way of dealing with inner and outer threats, and whether he is capable of coping adequately with a full knowledge of his condition.

If he tries to force us to answer before we are certain of our ground or before he seems ready, we may temporize with further tests or special examinations. When we decide to reply, either directly or by accepting his need for denial, we will do it in the light of as much understanding as possible of his adaptive method (and how effectively this works for him), of his cooperativeness and of his trust in us. We try to determine the likely course of his disease and whether he is making realistic plans. And we try to include his family in all these considerations, finding those responsible members upon whom he can rely, answering their questions appropriately, helping to reconcile their thinking with the patient's, and, not infrequently, assisting them with their grief.

Continued psychological management, following closely the organic course of the disease, often calls for great flexibility on the part of the physician. During periods of stability or relatively slow progression of the pathological process, the problems encountered may be no different from those in more benign, chronic illnesses. In these intervals many patients lose their acute preoccupation with their physical condition and again take part in the life around them. But we must expect recurrent crises to arise whenever new symptoms appear or when there is any increase of incapacity, accompanying surgery, and above all with intensified pain. Then anxiety surges up, defenses begin to crumble, and the patient can be rapidly overwhelmed by despair and imperative needs for relief, consideration, and protection. If physical and emotional support is not rapidly mobilized, there are risks of suicide, of flight from treatment (sometimes to seek impossible or quack cures), or, least dramatic but perhaps saddest of all, a retreat to utter loneliness and emptiness, a dying bereft of any consolation. To help avoid or to mitigate these tragedies and allow the patient to carry through to the end as best he can, tests all of the doctor's skill in understanding his patient somatically as well as psychologically, and permits him to apply his knowledge for the patient's sake in true medical tradition.

SUGGESTED READING

ADULT ADAPTATION: SOME CHARACTERISTIC FORMS IN MEN AND WOMEN

Berliner, B. (1947), On Some Psychodynamics of Masochism. *Psychoanalytic Quarterly*, 16:459-471. A useful approach to the complicated problem of masochism.

Pearson, G. H. J. & English, O. S. (1937), *Common Neuroses of Children and Adults* (New York: Norton).

Jones, E. (1916), The God Complex. *Essays in Applied Psychoanalysis*, 2:244-265 (New York: International Universities Press, 1964). A pioneer study of the narcissistic character.

MARRIAGE AND PREGNANCY

Bibring, G. L. (1959), Some Considerations of the Psychological Processes in Pregnancy. *The Psychoanalytic Study of the Child*, 14:113-127.

Bibring, G. L., Dwyer, T. F., Huntington, D. S., & Valenstein, A. F. (1961), A Study of the Psychological Processes in Pregnancy and the Earliest Mother-Child Relationship. *The Psychoanalytic Study of the Child*, 16:9-72.

Deutsch, H. (1944-1945), *The Psychology of Women*, Volume II on Motherhood (New York: Grune & Stratton).

AGING AND OLD AGE

Bibring, E. (1953), The Mechanism of Depression. In: *Affective Disorders*, ed. Phyllis Greenacre (New York: International Universities Press, pp. 13-48).

Bibring, G. L. (1966), Old Age: Its Liabilities and Its Assets. In: *Psychoanalysis—A General Psychology*, ed. R. M. Loewenstein, L. M. Newman, M. Schur, & A. J. Solnit (New York: International Universities Press, pp. 253-271).

Birren, J. E., ed. (1959), *Handbook of Aging and the Individual* (Chicago: University of Chicago Press). See especially: Von Mering, O. & Weniger, F. L., Social-Cultural Background of the Aging Individual, pp. 279-335; and Busse, E. W., Psychopathology, pp. 364-399.

Eissler, K. R. (1955), *The Psychiatrist and the Dying Patient* (New York: International Universities Press).

Freud, S. (1916-1917), Introductory Lectures on Psycho-Analysis (*Standard Edition*, Vols. 15 & 16). Jealousy, paranoia, and depression are discussed in Lectures XVI, XXIV, and XXVI.

Goldfarb, A. I. (1956), Psychotherapy of the Aged. *Psychoanalytic Review*, 43:68-81.

Hinton, J. (1967), *Dying* (Baltimore: Penguin Books).

Levin, S. (1965), Some Suggestions for Treating the Depressed Patient. *Psychoanalytic Quarterly*, 34:37-65.

Mendelson, M. (1960), *Psychoanalytic Concepts of Depression* (Springfield, Ill.: Charles C Thomas).

Payne, E. C., Jr. (1967), The Physician and the Patient Who Is Dying. In: *Psychodynamic Studies on Aging*, ed. S. Levin & R. J. Kahana (New York: International Universities Press, pp. 111-163).

Part V

MEDICAL PSYCHOTHERAPY

LECTURE

13

Psychotherapeutic Principles

In the course of outlining the maturation of individual personalities, tracing the interplay of drives, adaptive abilities, and experiences through the phases of life, we have illustrated some of the implications of this development for the care of our patients. To round out our discussion, and as a review, it might be helpful to examine more broadly and formulate explicitly the nature of medical psychotherapy as we see it, the application of psychological understanding in medical practice: What are its basic aims, principles, and techniques? How is it related to other forms of psychotherapy?

The different forms of dynamic or psychoanalytic psychotherapies have been characterized by the use of five basic therapeutic principles: *suggestion, abreaction, interpretation, clarification,* and *manipulation* (G. L. Bibring, 1947; E. Bibring, 1954).

Suggestion refers to the tendency in the patient to be influenced by the doctor in his thinking, feeling, and behavior independent of his rational judgment. It is based upon the remnant of childlike attitudes, an emotional readiness to accept the benign influence of his physician in the same way that as a child he gave credence, with unquestioning faith, to the authority of his parents; e.g., when he felt hurt or afflicted,

231

then mother or father soothed or kissed the injured place; they said it would feel better, and so it did. In medical psychotherapy, suggestion plays an important part in the patient's readiness to accept blindly his doctor's recommendations on trust alone before he has had the opportunity to test their validity.

The easing of distress afforded by *abreaction* is seen most impressively in patients with acute psychological trauma and anxiety states. It is more generally familiar as the ordinary discharge of feelings and the emotional relief, for instance, in talking out worries and fears, and in releasing stored-up anger. The case of Anna O., the first patient cited by Breuer and Freud (1893-1895), was one of the earliest classical examples to demonstrate the beneficial effect of abreaction (see Lecture 2).

Interpretation as it is used in psychoanalysis is aimed at increasing the patient's knowledge of himself, specifically of his heretofore unconscious attitudes and emotions, and his deeper wishful fantasies and defenses, those psychological elements which seem "unfit to be conscious" and are therefore repressed. Interpretation is employed only after the way has been prepared by mitigating the intensity of the patient's initial anxieties and inner resistances, while carefully gauging his equilibrium to avoid traumatizing him with premature confrontations. Both this preparatory effort and the actual interpretations require an intimate knowledge of the patient's psychological state at a given time, something that can hardly be gained except in a detailed, intensive psychotherapeutic study as is the case in psychoanalysis. Under these circumstances, where the patient consistently tries to express in words, without reservation or selection, all of his thoughts and feelings as they occur to him, and systematic attention can be paid to both the impulsive and defensive aspects of the patient's behavior, interpretation can lead to an effective uncovering and resolution of the childhood conflicts which underlie the neurotic illness. With it we can expect a strengthening of mature, more realistic adaptive tendencies in our patient.

In dynamic psychotherapies which also support adjustive changes but whose goals are less far-reaching, a different form of insight may be offered to help the patient appreciate objectively the significance of his preoccupations, conflicts, and behavior patterns, and of his perceptions and personal bias in relation to the people and issues important and close to him. This insight enables him to distinguish, with some greater emotional detachment, between the reality of events and their special meaning for him, to separate his own adult attitudes and judgments from his more childlike, neurotic conceptions, and to comprehend how all of this may be related to his problems. This principle is called *clarification:* the therapist clarifies psychological elements that are "fit to be conscious," that is, which are admissible to awareness without arousing too strong discomfort and resistance, or those which are already dimly known though not fully understood. Basically, clarification refers to what has been described in Lecture 2 as suppressed (in contrast to repressed), preconscious (in contrast to unconscious) psychological material.

Therapeutic manipulation, the fifth of these fundamental principles of treatment, has its leading application in short-term psychotherapy. This form of treatment is of the greatest importance in emergencies and psychological crisis situations, and it plays an essential role in preventive efforts to avoid serious psychological disturbances, and it is the method of choice in medical psychotherapy. It is the method which intrudes least into a patient's existing modes of adaptation. It designates our effort to help a patient, within the given framework of his emotional system, to master certain stress situations by utilizing his existing personality structure, enabling him to find and follow the ways by which he can function more satisfactorily and gain increasing security without having to go through a major psychological reorganization. Since the principle of therapeutic manipulation refers to the process that attempts to make better use of a patient's adaptive potentialities, and tries to achieve this with his co-operation and understanding, it should not be mistaken for applying trickery or taking over the running of the patient's life; albeit for honorable therapeutic purposes. It is a therapeutic intervention diverting the patient's inner strivings away from the existing neurotic complications and toward more constructive solutions. This principle has to be based upon careful evaluation and understanding of the patient's personality. Such understanding is of the greatest help in improving the doctor-patient relationship, and it can effect favorable changes in the patient's life situation even after a relatively small number of therapeutic sessions.

In psychoanalysis, which aims at the most extensive and profound changes, all these therapeutic principles are employed to a certain degree, but the leading role is reserved for interpretation of the detailed information gathered by free association, whereas deep interpretations are not helpful in most cases treated by psychotherapy with limited goals because of the nature of the treatment situation. Limited-goal psychotherapy, using the method of interviews rather than free association, may be indicated specifically because of a certain fragility of the patient's personality, as in some psychotic and borderline states, in severe psychosomatic conditions, and in patients of advanced age and with serious physical illnesses. Furthermore, this method of therapy is applied when a rigid, adverse reality situation might interfere or limit the results of extensive therapy beyond a certain point; and last but not least, when the patient's literal-mindedness or limited intelligence preclude a form of therapy that requires psychological insight and understanding. Limited-goal psychotherapy has an important place in the treatment of isolated symptoms that are predominantly due to acute stress rather than combined with long-standing personality trends; or, if the disturbance is due to a transitory developmental crisis like adolescent turmoil, it is often resolved by supportive therapy.

In goal-limited psychotherapy the doctor aims to stabilize and support the patient by dealing with current stresses. To give interpretations of deeply repressed material such as castration anxieties or incestuous fantasies is, in this form of treatment, unsound and may be harmful. Either the patient will reject them outright as absurd and foolish, or he may accept them as an intellectual conversation piece between himself and his doctor, without taking any further notice. Worst of all, if their impact goes beyond this point they may arouse strong anxieties in the patient without the therapist having adequate means at his disposal to deal with them as he would have in the cautious and protective psychoanalytic process. Under these circumstances the patient often takes flight and drops the physician.

With respect to the setting of goals, we cannot generalize about specific ones—these vary with the patient—but something can be said about the principles of establishing them. With growing experience a doctor frequently develops the ability to gain valuable impressions even in the first few interviews, as he becomes alerted to the patient's complaints, conflicts, and present-day situation, his family constellation and developmental sequence, his personality structure, and his life pattern. We assess his emotional and intellectual potentials, outline the danger spots, and arrive at a conclusion and a blueprint for therapy. Satisfactory as this often proves to be and tempting as this always is for our self-esteem, it may also lead to rather serious misconceptions and mismanagement if our judgments are premature and in error. There the flexibility of the therapist, his unfaltering attention, and his readiness to supplement, or if necessary to abandon his initial conclusions, and with these much of his initial goal and program, are indispensable for good therapy.

The duration of treatment in limited-goal psychotherapy is variable. Though many people expect it to be relatively brief, for certain patients, especially those with borderline states or with psychoses, or patients with severe psychosomatic illnesses, it is essential to carry on psychotherapy for many years, either steadily or intermittently. Some of these patients resemble those chronically ill and persistently depressed or overdependent individuals with somatic complaints, often with multiple and recurrent ailments, who are familiar to every physician and every outpatient clinic. The doctor's task is largely psychotherapeutic with many of these patients. He supports their adjustment to the demands life makes on them and has to do this over a long period, particularly in periods of crisis or acute disturbances. At the other extreme, an acute stress reaction may be resolved in a few therapeutic interviews. Adequate psychological management of anxieties arising in response to physical illness can frequently be carried out within the framework of medical practice, in the course of routine office visits or hospital rounds. The approach to managing or preventing psychological exigencies, utilizing these principles which are applicable in any field concerned with human difficulties—not only in medicine and psychiatry —is illustrated in the following case (G. L. Bibring, 1949).

A social agency requested psychiatric consultation about the marital and vocational problems of a thirty-year-old woman. Mrs. C. A.'s husband was a writer who had been employed steadily before their marriage, but since then had been working only irregularly. She on her part held a well-paying but rather strenuous job in a factory in order to provide for them both. She reported that she began to feel tired and one day she fainted at work without any demonstrable physical cause. She had turned to the agency to get help with a divorce because of her husband's infidelity and because she wanted advice about the kind of job that would not exhaust her as the last one did.

This woman had come from a nice family. She had three younger sisters whom she had almost always cared for, thus helping her mother who had been a chronic invalid. Through her high sense of responsibility and devotion she had become her father's favorite. In her teens, she fell in love with a musician. She gave him up because of her family's objections. They did not want her to marry an artist who might be an uncertain provider and not too reliable a husband. Subsequently she left home rather suddenly in order to look after her next younger unmarried sister who, unbeknownst to the rest of the family, had become pregnant. Mrs. C. A. took care of her sister and of the baby during this whole period. She was hard hit when the infant died shortly after the delivery. At this point she decided that her sister did not need her any longer and she felt ready to marry a writer who had pursued her unsuccessfully for quite some time. Her husband held a good job in an advertising firm, but when his wife went through an episode of depression he gave up his position to take care of her. When she recovered he returned to work, but after a short while Mrs. C. A. again became depressed and her husband, out of concern over her condition, remained at home with her. This time he did not resume employment again. This was the reason why Mrs. C. A. took up work in the factory and from then on she supported both of them. Her husband stayed at home, writing occasionally, with little success, and started to go out with other women.

Mrs. C. A. was an attractive, responsible, and competent person, and while her husband gave the impression of being less strong or effective, he too seemed a likable man of considerable artistic talent. The question the agency raised was whether a divorce was advisable and necessary or whether the wife could be helped to solve her problems in a less drastic way.

Mrs. C. A.'s history suggested a repetitive masochistic pattern in her life: she tended to sacrifice herself as she had done by taking care of her younger sisters when she herself was still a child, in order to help her mother, which then, in turn, gained her father's approval. Her desire to marry a struggling musician in her teens had a similar romantic sacrificial quality. After renouncing this man on her family's request she devoted herself again to a person in need of assistance—setting aside her own plans in order to help her sister through her illegitimate pregnancy. When this act of mercy was no longer necessary because of the death of the baby, she finally married, apparently bringing to an end her exclusive attention to her family's welfare.

This behavior impressed us as indicating a typical masochistic trend. One fact seemed especially significant for our evaluation of the problem that she presented to the agency: her husband had been a good worker before his marriage and it seemed that he was deteriorating under the influence of his wife's masochistic attitudes; she apparently provoked tendencies existing in him which he had under better control prior to his marriage. After all, he had tried to go back to work until she again interfered by becoming depressed, forcing him to stay at home and take care of her. Furthermore, it seemed to us that his self-indulgence, which she made possible, did not really provide adequate satisfaction for him, and that this could explain why he became restless in their marriage and looked for gratification with other women.

On the basis of this material it appeared very doubtful that Mrs. C. A. could come closer to solving her problems by a divorce, since it was most likely that she would repeat the same pattern, getting herself into similar situations. She would easily find other people who needed her help and who would evoke her self-sacrificial needs. Since Mrs. C. A.'s problem seemed urgent, requiring quick intervention, we proceeded as follows: no attempt was made to interpret deeply the childhood sources of this pattern, namely, her competitive striving for her mother's position in the family constellation in order to gain her father's attention; nor was any attempt made to explore further the self-punishing aspect of her masochistic behavior and whether it stemmed from feelings of guilt based on the hostile elements in this rivalry with mother. Instead, the social worker clarified for the patient her pattern of self-sacrifice, focusing on her possible wish to be accepted by her father as his responsible and helpful daughter. She was shown how once she had succeeded in this way with him, she then continued with this attitude in her relationship to her sister and later to her husband, whom she chose in spite of the earlier warning by her family that artists might be unreliable as husbands. Furthermore, Mrs. C. A. was told that a divorce would in all likelihood not help her to give up a pattern which had been firmly established since childhood. And altogether it would be a more appropriate step to see if she could work this problem out within the framework of her marriage.

The most important thing to decide was how to intervene so as to enable a patient with such tendencies to be less self-defeating. We tried to achieve this first by giving her full credit for the great effort she had to make to be the provider of the family, and for the difficulties created by her husband's infidelity, in the face of her struggle to create the most helpful conditions for his writing. We avoided carefully any sugges-tion to her that she should change the home situation for her own benefit and relief because in our opinion this could have run counter to her concept that she has to deserve love through suffering. Moreover, the suggestion of doing some-thing for her own benefit might stimulate the feeling of guilt and thus actually increase her sacrificial impulse. Instead, we emphasized those aspects which would help to restore her husband's better adjustment: the social worker made a special point to the patient that she was the one person who could help her husband fulfill his role again in which he had failed by permitting her to become the sole breadwinner; it seemed essential to let him assert himself as the provider, to re-establish his self-confidence and allow him to enjoy her trust in him, instead of his remaining dependent and self-indulgent under her protection.

This was not easy for Mrs. C. A. to accept, and she re-quired careful and repeated encouragement. She had to be supported by reminding her that she, after all, by her depressive episodes, had unwittingly interfered with her husband's readiness to take his appropriate position. In order to stabilize this new marital configuration we added a further recommendation. As there were no children in the family for whom she could care, we advised her to become a nurse's aide instead of a factory worker as she had been before, or to take training as a nursery school teacher. Through this we hoped that she could continue to fulfill her unconscious need to be of help and to sustain others. In the final result, by means of these interviews using clarification and therapeutic manipulation, the downhill movement in the life situation of these two people came to a halt, and improvement was maintained over a number of years.

14

Medical Psychotherapy

Having outlined these principles of psychotherapy and the general direction of the psychotherapeutic goals, let us turn specifically to their place in medical practice. From the beginning of your contact with your patient you try to establish an optimum working relationship with him, seeking to gain his cooperation for history taking, examinations, and any special diagnostic or operative procedures. You endeavor to insure his responsible participation in the medicinal, dietary, and physical treatments; and you try carefully to find the best ways to discuss his illness with him and his family. Even the person who is coping with his illness very adequately may become anxious at times, for instance, upon learning that he will need prolonged bedrest or must undergo a major operation. Even more so, when the patient's psychological equilibrium is disturbed under the impact of illness, through discomfort, exhaustion, incapacitation, and apprehension, then we must relieve his suffering as much as possible and prevent the development of extreme anxieties, neurotic reactions, or, in especially vulnerable cases, the danger of a psychotic episode.

In general, with the physically sick, the psychotherapeutic task is determined in part by the nature of the organic illness: how acute or prolonged; whether minor, severe, critical, or terminal; whether hospitalization is necessary; what complicated or painful diagnostic procedures or surgery may be required; which areas and systems and functions of the body are involved or impaired; must the patient give up important and satisfying activities or modify his habits; will he lose his normal position within the family or be forced to change his vocation; etc.

We may say that every *acute illness* tends to create a great deal of anxiety in the patient and in the people close to him: the most frequent initial response to acute illness is a transitory state of increased dependence upon the environment, which sooner or later gives way to his leading character-istic attitudes and defense mechanisms. Conscious and un-conscious fears and fantasies about illness are very active in the patient's mind during this period.

Hospitalization in itself is particularly upsetting to some persons, especially older people and young children. The separation from home and family, exposure to strange rooms, sounds, equipment, and smells, to other sick people and to bewildering numbers of medical personnel, and the interrup-tion of comforting daily routines with the imposition of different ones, all may contribute to this tension.

Episodes of confusion and delirium are often associated with acute phases of illness, particularly, as we discussed before, in the aged. Routine and minor procedures like blood tests, X-rays, cardiograms, and blood pressure determinations, as well as those which seem "uncanny" and more threatening to most patients, such as biopsies, intubations, endoscopies, spinal punctures, and many others, may temporarily add physical distress and, more importantly, subject the patient to the anxiety of awaiting their fateful results. At times, the great concern of the patient's family can add to his anxiety.

A degree of irritability, demandingness, or repetitive questioning in the early part of convalescence might be a feature of psychological readjustment after the trauma of illness, and with returning vigor the patient could become restless or aggressive in reaction to the limitations and monotony of the sickroom.

One of the frequent accompaniments of sickness, hospitalization, and states of exhaustion and physical depletion is a reactive depression, a mood of unhappiness, discouragement, and pessimism, which must not be confused with the more serious psychotic condition of melancholic depression (see Lecture 12). Depression is a basic affective reaction to disappointments, failures or losses, just as anxiety or fear is a primary response to danger from within or without. Illness might lead to this mood of despondency because of a man's concern that he might not get well again, or might never regain the necessary strength to provide for his family, or even on the basis of his idea that sickness equals moral weakness. There are a number of equivalents of depressive reactions which are apt to mask this emotional condition, such as apathy, fatigue, sleeplessness or lack of appetite, and there are a variety of defense mechanisms which different individuals apply in order to ward off the feeling of gloom. Depression can be hidden behind these defenses and then, to the surprise of the environment, it may come through at a time when the patient is making definite progress toward physical recovery. It seems as though when the pressure of his preoccupation with the acute physical illness has lifted, the patient relaxes his effort to hold back these emotions.

When the illness began early in life or has been very long-standing, it may influence the patient's personality development in the direction of dependent and demanding character traits or a masochistic attitude. Particularly if he is disabled or crippled, there is the risk that those taking care of him may respond as if he had literally become a child again, thus impeding any possible readjustment.

Ever so often patients as they get used to their long-standing illness display a kind of compensatory pride in their condition as something that sets them apart, but in a special way. They carry their suffering and courage as a badge which entitles them to be the center of attention. They may have become estranged from their families and the hospital may represent a second home. Among such patients some show a quite unexpected reaction: if a radical improvement in their condition can be achieved by skillful medical or surgical procedures, for example, by heart surgery, we may find that these patients feel almost deprived of their painfully acquired status as very sick people and of all the care and attention which was accorded to them, and they may have the greatest difficulty in accepting a normal, healthy life.

However, in most patients with chronic illness there lives the hope of being rewarded by a final cure if they accept the treatment with fortitude. But if the symptoms continue without letup, many react with anger, despair or apathy, and with an almost spiteful inclination to sabotage their treatment altogether.

The *surgical* patient's normal apprehension prior to operation is part of a necessary psychological adjustment. The prospect of an operation is almost always experienced as a threat to one's life. Additional fears of loss of control, helplessness, paralysis, and suffocation may be evoked by various kinds of anesthesia. There is apprehension of operative and postoperative pain. Impending loss or alteration of a part of the body arouses basic fear of mutilation. When an organ acquires special symbolic meaning for the patient, even a minor operation, as the surgeon judges it, may create particularly intense anxiety as in the case of Mr. K., the Navy Yard laborer (Lecture 6).

In general, surgery of the eyes, reproductive organs, heart, or brain, facial or other visible plastic procedures, amputation of a limb, or the production of artificial stomata evoke the greatest dread. The patient's preoperative fears may be increased by previous experiences of surgery in childhood. Fantasies from childhood years may be vastly more disturbing than any realistic threat: like those which link the operation with ideas of mutilation or sexual attacks.

In contrast to these cases, an operation may be experienced as an atonement for conscious or unconscious guilt feelings, a mechanism among certain patients who seem to insist upon surgery, especially of a cosmetic type, even against their doctor's advice. For example, Eric, the adolescent boy who requested surgery because he was convinced that his ears stood out in an ugly fashion, was driven by guilt and anxiety over masturbation (see Lecture 5). Sometimes the surgeon is startled to discover that although the patient has almost forced this elective surgery, he subsequently complains excessively and unduly, implying that this procedure made him infinitely worse than he was before and should be repaired by an additional operation. An operation requested because of unconscious feelings of guilt (i.e., of a need for punishment) rarely can solve the underlying conflict. Instead, more often than not, the persisting conflict leads to intense dissatisfaction with the results, complicated by the fact that now the responsibility for this "punishment" can be shifted from the old childhood figures onto the surgeon.

In our experience these reactions can present a serious risk in cosmetic surgery and they should be carefully evaluated beforehand, especially if it seems to the surgeon that the urgency of the patient's wish is not in keeping with the objective defect. There are other signs which should warn the physician of impending trouble: in the complete absence of appropriate anxiety (as we saw in the case of Neil, our high school football hero, Lecture 8), or if the response is excessive or incongruous, the surgeon should be alerted to the necessity of preparing the patient more adequately for the procedure, and if it seems advisable, of calling in a psychiatric specialist.

The medical psychotherapeutic approach to these patients, as in any others, varies with the personality structure of the individual (Kahana and Bibring, 1964). As we followed the developmental phases step by step in earlier lectures, we indicated how impulses, stressful experiences, adaptive efforts and conflicts, all stemming from specific stages of this development, may shape the behavior of grownups, including their reactions to illness. We have attempted to describe some models of adult personalities, reflecting different steps in this development. It is impossible to categorize the almost endless variety and to label and elaborate all the conceivable formations. We have tried to describe those types whom we encounter most frequently and whose psychological mechanisms are best known to us. Even then we have to emphasize that they rarely appear in this clear-cut, exclusive form, but there are transitions between these configurations and combinations (the cases of two men with myocardial infarctions [Lecture 9] illustrate combined or intermediate personality types). Growing experience in observing and dealing with patients will help fill in many gaps, and permit increasing flexibility and freedom to individualize, to elaborate, and to broaden these sketches.

To summarize our previous discussions:

For the overdependent and demanding *oral* personality, being sick means that once more he might, as in infancy, receive the limitless care and attention for which he longs; but at the same time it brings the threat that he may be neglected coldly and even abandoned to starve helplessly (see Lecture 3). The main task that the psychological management of such a patient requires of the physicians, nurses, and all who attend him is to reassure him of their readiness to meet his needs as fully as possible, and if the setting of limits becomes necessary because his claims escalate, to present this to him reasonably and impersonally rather than in a state of exasperation which will be perceived as rejection and punishment.

Illness threatens the rational, well-organized, and self-disciplined *compulsive* patient with loss of control over aggressive, disorderly, and self-indulgent impulses (see Lecture 4). He fights against them by becoming even more responsible and self-restrained to the extent of inflexibility, and his determination borders upon obstinacy. In the effort to help him gain a better adjustment to the necessary medical management, we encourage his active, intelligent participation in our deliberations and planning. He should be informed systematically about his illness and treatment so that he can apply his logical, rational approach, and we give him full credit for his sound reasoning and methodical way of dealing with things. We have to maintain our understanding tolerance for the hypersensitive reaction of this kind of patient, who may be inclined to experience the slightest irregularity in hospital procedures as sloppiness or negligence. In discussing with him such complaints arising out of his overconcern, it is not helpful to defend the position of the hospital adamantly. It is better to concede to the patient whatever in his observations is correct, yet, at the same time, we will put this in the right perspective by pointing out a more objective and tolerant evaluation and placing it into the framework of the positive aspects of the care which he receives.

To the emotionally susceptible, anxiety-prone, dramatizing, captivating, *hysterical* personality, an infirmity may feel like a disaster, a freakishness, a complete failure, or a punishment (see Lecture 6). Patients of this type are inclined to deny and repress everything that arouses their neurotic anxiety. Men try to protect themselves against anything that they believe may diminish their manliness, by emphasizing their physical strength, virility, and courage, especially before women on the medical team. Women patients fearing loss of their attractiveness may seek attention seductively and flirtatiously. In the face of this response it is essential that the physician keep in mind the central significance which these issues have for the patient and carefully avoid making light of them. At the same time he should be alert to this person's anxiety, which may be concealed behind protective denial or counterphobic swagger, and avoid stirring up emotional storms toward which these patients have an inclination. In contrast to the completeness of explanations offered to the compulsive personality, those given to this type of patient are less systematic and detailed. Rather, they focus upon dispelling the irrational, frightening fantasies. At times this type of patient should be given the opportunity of talking about his anxieties, thus allowing discharge of his constrained fears and providing emotional relief. Particularly with patients of the opposite sex the physician must preserve a delicate balance, on the one hand indicating his appreciation of their feminine or masculine assets without overemphasizing them and thus stimulating their erotic fantasies; on the other hand, the physician must carefully maintain a certain objectivity without becoming too reserved or defensively cool.

Illness and medical care for the reserved, shy, and aloof *schizoid* personality can mean an intrusion into his preferred privacy and, more than that, a painful and possibly dangerous disturbance of his emotional equilibrium and psychological integration (see Lecture 8). He tries to deal with this by further withdrawal or by denying his sickness just as he has learned to protect himself from earlier hurts and deep personal experiences of disappointment. Good medical management requires our acceptance of his retiring attitude, not demanding or prodding him to be sociable and responsive; but good medical management also requires that we continue to show him our interest, our concern, and our wish to be of help. In this way we might reach him and give him confidence in the environment as a protective and benign one.

The *narcissistic* patient feels superior and often shows arrogance and even grandiosity (see Lecture 9). He will accept the judgment of only the most distinguished physician in the hierarchy of the hospital, keeping a sharp lookout for any flaws in this doctor's performance and valuing his own opinion above medical advice. Sickness menaces his sense of invulnerability and increases his overcompensating behavior. He will be most secure if we give him recognition, directly or tacitly, as worthy of our respect, avoiding anything which he might experience as belittling him, like a well-meaning but patronizing attitude. Yet it is equally necessary to do this without any concession as far as our own professional competence and standing are concerned. This type of patient is deeply afraid of being failed through mediocrity and lack of skill. He must be the important patient of an equally outstanding doctor.

The *masochistic* personality type has great difficulties in accepting medical help simply and directly (see Lecture 10). He or she must demonstrate and emphasize distress and suffering, and frequently reacts with irritation and fights attempts at reassurance. The doctor who understands this behavior will be less likely to feel frustrated by the masochistic patient's paradoxical reaction to optimistic statements or to any tangible improvement. Instead of emphasizing his pleasure over the patient's improvement, he must first of all acknowledge sympathetically the pains and difficulties created by the illness. Whereas normally one stresses the positive results of treatment, with this kind of patient one tends rather to concentrate upon appreciating the effort that he has to make in order to get well. It is sometimes even helpful when talking about recovery, to emphasize the gain that his improvement will bring to his family and environment rather than only to him personally.

The mistrustful, guarded, or self-righteously aggressive, the *paranoid* person feels that his illness is due to the fault and lack of consideration or even the maliciousness of others (see Lecture 12). He is oversensitive and expects the worst from everyone. It is generally useless to try to convince him directly by defending our good intentions. It is essential to let him know what procedures are planned and which medications are offered. Introduction of reality factors can counteract his suspicious fantasies, so he is not taken unawares, but can prepare himself by reasoning it out, either on his own or through arguing with his environment. When he fights us, it is imperative at this point not to be drawn into the battle with the patient, to avoid reacting with annoyance to his mistrust, but rather to meet his suspiciousness and agitation with an unhurried, thoughtful, considerate, but firm and impartial recommendation of the necessary medical procedures. In our experience that is a reliable way of establishing a more trusting relationship between the patient and his doctor.

15

Establishing the Doctor-Patient Relationship

The physician can usually learn a great deal about a patient's personality even during the first visit as he follows his regular plan of history taking and examinations. Although the patient's *chief complaint* expresses his conscious motivation for seeking help, his way of stating it, whether pleasingly or indifferently, guardedly or with meticulous attention to detail, gives one important psychological information.

The *history of the present illness* and a survey of the facets of the patient's life often shed light on his emotional reactions to illness as well as on the way in which he is used to dealing with these reactions. They also may reveal psychological stresses which are predisposing or play a part in precipitating his organic condition.

In the medical history the *occupational* section provides information on the strength of his personality in adjusting to the demands made by life and reality on him, in terms of the patient's capacity to work steadily, reliably, and productively, and his ability to establish mature personal relationships in social groups.

The *dietary* portion of the medical history includes a description of special reactions to food and his ability to maintain control over his diet at the same time as it sheds light on a wide variety of physical disorders. The reported eating habits may reveal the urgency of the patient's needs for gratification and his intolerance of tension. His food intake may vary with mood changes or be related to the feeling of security.

As a *past medical history* of rheumatic fever in childhood is important in the differential diagnosis of heart disease, it also points toward the emotional problems that such childhood illnesses create. It may provide the clue to an early period of anxiety or receiving and expecting special attention. It may, for example, carry the meaning of having been sent away from home to a hospital while "more favored" brothers and sisters were not separated from the parents; this might have been especially important if it coincided with a crucial time in the patient's psychological development like the birth of a sibling or the death of an important member of the family.

The *family history*, which provides information about hereditary and infectious diseases, often has additional importance for the understanding and handling of a case. The patient's general disposition toward his illness, such as stoicism or the tendency to complain, may be modeled upon the attitude of one of his parents. Conversion symptoms frequently are based upon identification with a member of the family to whom the patient has a close emotional tie. A common instance is the widow who develops chest pain while grieving over her husband who died of a heart attack, and this may occur on the anniversary of his death.

When children or aged persons are treated, and in the management of very serious or disabling or terminal illnesses, relatives may give essential support. Yet, as we often see in mental and psychosomatic disorders, the family may also be a major source of stress. In turn, the patient's incapacity can have an adverse effect—personal, social, or economic—upon the family members: they too deserve our consideration and may need our counsel. So that when we request the help of a family member for our patient, it is equally important to take into account the personality of this relative and in what way he might be able to deal most effectively with the patient. This, for instance, is paramount in setting up a program of home care. In all these circumstances it can be helpful to learn whether the family is large or small, cohesive or scattered and isolated, and whether the home atmosphere is peacefully stimulating, or unstable and unsettling.

In this manner psychological information can be found in any part of the medical anamnesis from the patient's *age* and *place of residence* through the entire *review of organ systems*. Often data disclosed in one part of the history are extended and confirmed in others. Thus, the picture of a man's sexual adjustment may be obtained through the marital history, in a discussion of his adolescence, or as a result of the direct review of his genitourinary functions.

The doctor's sympathetic interest, objectivity, capacity to understand his patient's attitudes, and his tolerance of the patient's strongly expressed feelings are as important as special techniques of interviewing. Certain considerations are pertinent to skillful psychological observation and medical psychotherapy. Whereas organic illness can often be diagnosed and treated even in a relatively antagonistic patient, a positive atmosphere is usually more productive for a medical-psychological interview. For example, with an anxious or oversensitive patient it may be essential to concentrate first of all upon establishing a secure and comfortable relationship. With a dependent person the doctor should be prepared to show his willingness to take the patient's needs and demands seriously, though he may have to admit that not all of them can be fulfilled. While conditions of privacy and the maintenance of confidentiality are always essential, they may become the center of concern for the patient who is mistrustful, is burdened by guilt feelings, or who suffers from a strong sense of shame and embarrassment. And thus we must be equally ready to meet other kinds of patients on their own terms.

As beginners in interviewing we tend to rely more upon an established "outline" of the history to guide ourselves (Rosenbaum, Jacobs, and Oxenhorn, 1968). With increasing experience and knowledge we know what to listen for or to ask, and we gain the freedom to let the patient follow his own course while we organize the information coherently. When the patient is prepared to give us his confidence, it is rarely necessary to push hard for additional material. He will move on his own to related subjects which contain important additional data.

When we interview, we always keep at the back of our minds what we have learned about the important phases of human development, so that we are immediately alerted to any material which might be particularly significant. For example, we know the importance of an illness of the mother during the patient's early childhood, of sibling rivalry, the oedipal phase or the period of turmoil in adolescence. Whenever the material begins to approach these crucial issues, we try to let it come through as completely as possible by allowing sufficient time and not interrupting the patient with distracting questions.

As a rule, when direct inquiry is indicated, our questions should be of a general nature at first, that is to say, not too specific or pointed, in order to avoid arousing resistance or defensiveness before we have any possibility of assessing the patient's tolerance and his areas of greatest sensitivity, and this cautious approach tends to elicit a more spontaneous and reliable history. Usually the doctor tries to conduct the interview so that it does not become too intense and painful for his patient. This should not lead to the mistake of overlooking those instances where a patient is under great stress but will benefit from expressing his feelings to the doctor and is ready to do so.

Some doctors shy away from such confrontations because of their own sensitivity when it comes to a patient's anguish and unhappiness. In our opinion, this can be mastered with knowledge and experience, just as any physician can tolerate the physical suffering of his patients once he has learned to understand and treat the physical illness. Instead of shutting off the patient's communication because of his own discomfort the knowledgeable doctor can listen sympathetically and can use his understanding to help the patient with emotional distress.

We stated that a psychologically meaningful history can be taken, observations of behavior can be made, and medical psychotherapy can be initiated within the usual framework of a thorough medical examination. Sometimes it is necessary to provide specifically for more extensive history taking or discussion of emotional problems. Occasionally this requires a few additional interviews. When the doctor understands his patient's problem and feels free to modify his approach suitably, he is less likely to find that "there is not enough time" for this kind of medical management. It is our experience that even very busy physicians in general practice who suffer from the pressure and tempo of their professional activities feel relieved and satisfied after they have acquired the basic understanding and skill for medical psychotherapy. They find that some of their sense of harassment was due to the feeling of frustration, for instance, with patients who made many demands, requested repeated emergency visits, and habitually failed to follow recommendations, etc.

The seemingly intractable patients pursue their doctors because something in their psychological needs is not taken care of. Many of their somatic symptoms are based upon anxiety or chronic depression. It finally may turn out that what threatened to become too great an amount of energy spent on them in a comprehensive approach will, in the sum total, save the doctor time and worry, and prove to be actually more satisfactory for both patient and doctor.

Often, without becoming consciously aware of it, the patient will react to the doctor's presence and activity with *transference* feelings, in the same way that he did to his parents by whom he felt protected and guarded and who gave him intimate physical attention in early childhood; or his reaction might reflect more negative feelings of being neglected and rejected. This supersedes his realistic reaction to the doctor as a trained and skilled professional person. In order to appreciate better this transference material let us present some observations of a case from psychiatric practice —a case where the repetition of a patient's attitude toward certain people "in authority," including the doctor, represented a leading feature.

A young, intelligent girl came to consult the doctor about anxiety which she experienced when she was in a crowd, sleeplessness, and long-lasting work difficulties. She was doubtful whether or not she should start psychotherapy and she expected advice. In this first interview she spoke about her very unsatisfactory attempts with several psychiatrists to solve this problem. The first psychiatrist, she complained, was so tactless and inquisitive that she felt that she could not stand working with him. His remarks which she quoted sounded somewhat too direct and not carefully chosen for a first interview, but it was not certain that the patient did not exaggerate: this doctor was known as a skillful specialist and one would have expected him to act more subtly. The second physician whom she had consulted was, in her opinion, too simple, not bright enough for her liking. It was true that the patient was a very intelligent young woman, yet that would not justify her demand for a genius as her doctor. Her third experience was unsuccessful because, after the first conversation, she had the impression that the doctor was too interested in money when the question of fees was discussed.

For a moment one might have been tempted into accepting her story as a realistic appraisal without giving it further attention. But the doctor was interested in a certain aspect of this problem: how did it come about that the patient's contact with three rather different physicians, each with a good professional reputation, had led to the same negative result? Why did she find such severe fault with all of them that she decided against starting treatment? Although it was not immediately possible to answer this question, one could suspect a pattern in the patient's reactions, and accordingly, this psychiatrist—the fourth in the series—raised the question? "What do you think will be your complaints about me when you drop our next appointment?"

The patient was startled and denied any intention of this kind. However, when she was shown the similarity in her behavior toward these three different consultants, and it was suggested that such repetitive experiences may be due to some attitudes within herself and not so much within the other persons, she admitted two things: first, that today on her way to the appointment she had wondered whether it would be wise to go to this foreign-born psychiatrist who might not know enough about the life of an American college girl to be competent to judge her problems correctly; and secondly, that she had really had many other similar experiences of quick disappointments throughout her life. For example, the same thing had happened with music teachers: she could not start learning to play an instrument because after the first arrangements she consistently found the teacher inadequate and tried to find somebody better and more competent, until she gave up her search completely. Likewise, her other studies were affected in this way. She went from one famous school to another. There was always something that disappointed her, and it was only by chance and circumstances that she was finally forced to settle in one place, where she then finished her education.

This initial confrontation with her pattern was sufficient to give her some perspective, and with it to forestall the repetition of this behavior. It took quite some time for the doctor and the patient to understand fully why she repeated this attitude in all the different circumstances. She had been the younger of two children, a beautiful girl, much admired in the community where she lived; whereas her brother, four years older, was known for his special intelligence. The two had a very friendly relationship until a younger sister was born. From that time on—she was then six—our patient lost her pleasure in her own beauty: she met a successful rival in the person of this cute, new baby. She turned to other satisfactions and started to develop an extraordinary intellectual ambition, which led to intense competition with her older brother. Yet there too she could not succeed since she could not truly outdo him. She became the best pupil in her class, but that did not solve the problem since he still remained the top student in his much higher grade. Slowly her rivalry turned into a kind of obsession. When her brother took up chess, for instance, she secretly studied books about the game to surprise everybody with her superior ability when she finally began to play it openly. Or, whenever somebody asked a difficult question, she tried to look up information about it more quickly than her brother, and she thus became quite a little nuisance, much teased and laughed at in her family.

Then something happened which deeply affected the outcome of this conflict. In adolescence, her brother contracted poliomyelitis and became severely disabled. From that time on the patient could not remember any further feelings of jealousy. Instead she began to admire him—perhaps even to idealize him—to support him in his studies and to help him with his exams. She repressed her former negative feelings completely with regard to him, but she transferred the conflict with her brother onto anybody else who was fit to represent this figure for her. This included anyone who by his position, function, or personality reminded her unconsciously of her superior, older rival; and that was why, without seeing any of these connections and without understanding why she acted this way, she had to outdo all her teachers, superiors, colleagues, and doctors. This transference pattern influenced her to look for capable people, only to depreciate them when she encountered them. By doing so she could temporarily regain some feeling of superiority.

The tendency to transfer our childhood attitudes increases in neuroses where the inner conflicts are especially strong, and it is equally intensified if a person, through stress and trauma, feels helpless and dependent, as if he were a child again. This is an occurrence which we, as doctors, observe in almost all our patients. In accordance with the main development of his relationship to early parental figures he may see the physician, for example, as protective, devoted, all-powerful, punishing, remote, or even threatening. The patient may want to be cared for completely, fussed over, told what to do, or taken seriously enough to be included in the plan for his therapy, allowed as much as possible to work things out for himself like an independent, respected person, or be treated as an especially favored or attractive or brave individual. By carefully noting the transference as it appears in his relation to us we can add very important information to whatever we have learned from his history. This is one of the principal clues that can be of help in our specific approach to each patient. Moreover, understanding the character of transference gives us perspective, teaches us to take the behavior of the patient less personally but predominantly as a repetition of essential attitudes toward figures from the past.

By not letting ourselves be caught up in something that has little to do with us realistically we will be less prone to react too sensitively if the patient's transference has a negative quality, or equally, of becoming personally overinvolved in a patient's positive transference. We can then avoid playing into the repetitive behavior or we can clarify it for the patient as in the case of the young girl just described. Long before the full meaning of her behavior was understood by us it could be shown that she had attempted to depreciate one doctor after the other without sufficient objective reasons and that one now might expect that she would repeat this with her present therapist. Thus she was helped to deal more appropriately with this tendency which, up to then, had interfered completely with therapy.

Although the role of the physician differs greatly from that of his patient, he too can be involved in repeating with his patients early patterns of his relationships, especially if his own emotional problems are provoked and tested by his patient's transference manifestations. These *countertransference* responses when excessive can interfere with effective medical management. They mostly take the form of reinforcing defensively and rigidly the existing habitual "bedside manner" with little relation to the patient's specific emotional needs. Or they result in overinvolvement with loss of objectivity, taking expressions of transference literally and becoming entangled in the patient's emotional responses, reacting with unwarranted feelings of preference or aversion (G. L. Bibring, 1956).

Stereotyped bedside manners such as the invariably "warm and understanding," "the strong and reserved," "the calm and scientific," "the jovial," "the charming," "the learned and authoritative," or "the wise and crusty" kind of physician, have the effect of frustrating the patient's hope of being understood, and leaving him feeling alone and isolated, unless they chance to be appropriate for this particular person. Excessive responses of involvement may arise from a meeting of similar leanings in doctor and patient.

The appeal of a hysterical type of woman with her romantic disposition tends to stimulate a doctor's childhood daydreams of being superman in gleaming armor (man in white) who rescues the princess, mind you in the most proper way, from a dull and unrefined husband—dragon. Desires for miracles in the sick person may evoke omnipotent fantasies in the physician. Competitive strivings in aggressive patients can bring to the fore repressed rivalry or anxious insecurity in the doctor. We could continue with many similar instances, keeping in mind that we are referring to reactions based upon unconscious attitudes. Sometimes it is apparent that "countertransference" is not only aroused by the patient's transference but can represent largely the expression of the physician's personal, prevalent conflicts.

A woman pediatrician, skillful and dependable in her work with difficult children, especially children with behavior problems, showed one definite limitation: her achievements were marred by a very unpleasant relationship with the mothers of her patients. She started with an enthusiastic, very warm approach to each of them, which led to a short period of almost too much intimacy and friendship where the mother confided many things she should perhaps better have kept to herself. Then came a phase during which the doctor tried first in a very friendly way, then more and more aggressively, to relate these confessed weaknesses to the child's difficulties, and practically any concern the mother expressed about her child ended in a heated discussion about the mother's "faulty behavior." Invariably unpleasant scenes followed, with the distressed mother complaining bitterly that she would not work with the doctor under these circumstances.

This young pediatrician was not aware of the fact that she acted out her own problems. She was one of the people who had not settled their conflicts with their own mothers in childhood and adolescence. Each new child patient provoked and revived that old struggle. She immediately identified with the child in terms of her own early conflicts and tried to involve the parent intensely, to establish a friendship representing her longing for a fond relationship to her own mother. At the same time unconsciously she felt impelled to prove the "injustice" done to this child and all the children including herself when she was young.

In order to avoid such predicaments in their professional work it is helpful for doctors to observe carefully their own leading reactions toward the spectrum of personalities, so that they can become aware of any conspicuously repetitive difficulties with certain types of patients. It is additionally helpful to compare these difficulties with the reactions of colleagues to the same kind of patients, either to find out that they encounter the same problems or to discover that they can get along with these patients easily. In the former instance, it may be that the problems are essentially objective ones and hard to avoid, while in the latter case you may gain some awareness of the obstacles created by your countertransference.

The therapeutic importance of the doctor-patient relationship, as it has been emphasized for all aspects of medical management, has particular significance in dealing with psychosomatic disorders. We have in mind not only cases of peptic ulcer, hypertension, ulcerative colitis, hyperthyroidism, bronchial asthma, and other illnesses in which psychological stress influences physiological systems, but also some patients with disorders of organic origin who respond sensitively to emotional experiences with exacerbations or remissions of their symptoms. It appears to be the converging opinion of physicians with broad experience in psychosomatic disorders that the predisposing, underlying psychological disturbances began in very early periods of the child's development. The events that precipitate worsening of such conditions often involve actual or threatened separation from important figures upon whom they crucially depend. Thus it is often important to understand the part that family members may play in generating and maintaining these illnesses.

In the transference relationship the physician readily comes to represent such a key figure, usually the mother. This can be seen in a most dramatic form in acute disturbances, as in ulcerative colitis, when the patient, in response to an absence of his doctor, may become unreasonably demanding, with sudden increase of diarrhea, bleeding or weight loss. Close personal attention by the physician in daily visits, his availability during crises of illness, and the availability of other caretaking figures like nurses, dieticians, and other medical personnel, preparation of patients for separations, and general efforts to minimize frustrations and maintain a positive relationship, become essential in these cases. Consultation and team work with psychiatrists who have experience in managing psychosomatic disorders may be advisable. This leads to a question which arises not only in this group of illnesses but under many circumstances, namely: when should a patient be managed in medical psychotherapy by his physician, and when is treatment by a psychiatrist indicated?

The need for psychiatric consultation is often clearly apparent in emergencies of intense mental suffering, psychotic personality disorganization, suicidal impulses or aggressive outbursts toward others. It is sometimes more difficult to detect incipient crises or to pick up neurotic conditions. Quite profound depressions may be obscured by somatic symptoms or presented exclusively as a state of fatigue, and may be warded off by overworking, overeating, withdrawal, or excessive sleeping. Patients may preserve a precarious adjustment by unobtrusively restricting their activities as do those with phobias who shun crowds, restaurants or traveling in order to avoid situations which might give rise to panic. Others have to carry out exhausting rituals in secret, as obsessional neurotics must in order to meet their daily tasks. Still others deal with their anxiety and insecurity by using alcohol or drugs, or quietly struggle against emotionally determined sexual or work difficulties which prevent them from adequate functioning and achievements. Organic disease may overshadow a coexisting neurotic condition so that it is difficult to detect the emotional component which, nevertheless, influences the symptomatology one way or the other.

In these complicated cases one has to pay attention to any indications, however slight, of incongruous anxiety or depression, or to any previous emotional disturbances. If there is any doubt, the possibility is open to discuss the situation with a psychiatric consultant. It then can be decided whether referral to a psychiatrist or further psychotherapeutic work with the physician is the method of choice. Sometimes psychiatric referral, though indicated, will have to be post-poned, for instance, when a severe, urgent physical condition makes additional psychiatric intervention ill-advised, or with patients who require a long, careful period of preparation for psychiatric help because of their marked fear or shame—an attitude which unfortunately, much too often, interferes with appropriate treatment. The difficulties of such preparation and subsequent referral are increased if the physician has not yet overcome his own anxious prejudices, a state of affairs which one also finds not infrequently.

It has been the intention of these lectures on medical psychology to provide essential background knowledge of personality development. This can serve as a basis for the doctor's growing awareness of what goes on psychologically in himself and in his patients. This knowledge in turn leads to the refinement of his diagnostic acumen and to the improve-ment of his skill in managing his patients and their emotional reactions to physical illness. With a medical psychotherapeu-tic approach appropriate to different personalities, the physi-cian can aid his patients in preventing undue reactions to stress by supporting them through a sometimes extremely rough course of illness and convalescence, by detecting any serious neurotic disturbance, and by aiming at a sound decision and technique of psychiatric referral when this seems neces-sary. Just as the physician's medical abilities grow as he ac-cumulates experience, his psychological skills develop so that what might appear in the beginning to be an awesome assign-ment will, in the course of years, become his highly satis-factory competence.

SUGGESTED READING

PSYCHOTHERAPEUTIC PRINCIPLES

Bibring, E. (1954), Psychoanalysis and the Dynamic Psychotherapies. *Journal of the American Psychoanalytic Association*, 2:745-770. A systematic discussion of psychotherapeutic principles.

Knight, R. P. (1949), A Critique of the Present Status of the Psychotherapies. *Bulletin of the New York Academy of Medicine*, 25:100-114. Classifies psychotherapies according to their aims.

Levine, M. (1942), *Psychotherapy in Medical Practice* (New York: Macmillan). Describes psychotherapeutic techniques suitable for use in the course of regular medical practice.

MEDICAL PSYCHOTHERAPY

Binger, C. (1945), *The Doctor's Job* (New York: Norton). Discusses modern medicine and psychiatry as they affect the patient.

Pinner, M. & Miller, B. F. (1952), *When Doctors Are Patients* (New York: Norton). Over thirty autobiographical accounts of responses to different illnesses.

Prange, A. J., Jr. & Abse, D. W. (1957), Psychic Events Accompanying an Attack of Poliomyelitis. *British Journal of Medical Psychology*, 30:75-87. A psychological study of a severe physical illness suffered by one of the authors.

Titchener, J. L. & Levine, M. (1960), *Surgery As a Human Experience* (New York: Oxford University Press).

ESTABLISHING THE DOCTOR-PATIENT RELATIONSHIP

Alexander, F. (1950). *Psychosomatic Medicine* (New York: Norton).

Balint, M. (1957), *The Doctor, His Patient, and the Illness* (New York: International Universities Press). A study of the doctor-patient relationship in general medical practice.

Bird, B. (1955), *Talking with Patients* (Philadelphia: Lippincott). A concise introduction to interviewing of adults and children in a variety of clinical situations.

Deutsch, F. (1939), The Choice of Organ in Organ Neurosis. *International Journal of Psycho-Analysis*, 20:252-262. Considers the chain of etiological factors in psychosomatic disease.

Engel, G. L. (1955), Studies of Ulcerative Colitis: III. The Nature of the Psychologic Process. *American Journal of Medicine*, 19:231-256.

Freud, S. (1916-1917), Introductory Lectures on Psycho-Analysis. Lectures XXVII and XXVIII on the transference (*Standard Edition*, 16:431-463).

Mirsky, I. A. (1958), Physiologic, Psychologic and Social Determinants in the Etiology of Duodenal Ulcer. *American Journal of Digestive Diseases*, 3:285-314.

Whitehorn, J. C. (1944), Guide to Interviewing and Clinical Personality Study. *Archives of Neurology and Psychiatry*, 52:197-216. A systematic approach to the special psychiatric examination.

Reference Works

Arieti, S., editor (1959, 1966), *American Handbook of Psychiatry*. New York: Basic Books. Covers a wide range of applications of psychiatry.

Bellak, L., editor (1952), *Psychology of Physical Illness*. New York: Grune & Stratton. Articles pertaining to the psychological problems encountered in different medical specialties.

Brenner, C. (1955), *An Elementary Textbook of Psychoanalysis*. New York: International Universities Press.

Clyne, M. B. (1961), *Night Calls: A Study in General Practice*. London: Tavistock Publications.

Dwyer, T. F. (1968), Psychoanalytic Teaching in the Medical School. In: *The Teaching of Dynamic Psychiatry*, ed. G. L. Bibring. New York: International Universities Press, pp. 23-37.

Ewalt, J. R. & Farnsworth, D. L. (1963), *A Textbook of Psychiatry*. New York: McGraw Hill.

Fraiberg, S. H. (1959), *The Magic Years*. New York: Scribner's. Child development for parents.

Freud, S. (1917), Mourning and Melancholia. In: *The Standard Edition*, 14:237-258. London: The Hogarth Press, 1957.

Gill, M. M., Newman, R. and Redlich, F. C. (1954), *The Initial Interview in Psychiatric Practice*. New York: International Universities Press.

Grinstein, A. (1956-1966), *The Index of Psychoanalytic Writings*, 9 Vols. New York: International Universities Press. The standard bibliographical work in this field.

Henderson, D., Gillespie, R. D., & Batchelor, I. R. C. (1962), *A Textbook of Psychiatry for Students and Practitioners*, 9th ed. New York: Oxford University Press.

Hendrick, I. (1958), *Facts and Theories of Psychoanalysis*, 3rd ed. New York: Knopf.

Hinsie, L. E. and Campbell, R. J. (1960), *Psychiatric Dictionary*, 3rd ed. New York: Oxford University Press.

Jones, E. (1953, 1955 and 1957), *The Life and Work of Sigmund Freud*. 3 vols. New York: Basic Books, Inc.

Kaufman, M. R., Franzblau, A. N. & Kairys, D. (1956), The Emotional Impact of Ward Rounds. *J. Mount Sinai Hospital*, 23:782-803.

Kaufman, M. R., editor (1965), *The Psychiatric Unit in a General Hospital*. New York: International Universities Press. A symposium on the in-patient psychiatric service.

Linn, L., editor (1961), *Frontiers in General Hospital Psychiatry*. New York: International Universities Press. Thirty-six articles describing a variety of developments in more than a dozen countries around the world.

Lipowski, Z. J. (1967), Review of Consultation Psychiatry and Psychosomatic Medicine. *Psychosomatic Medicine*, 29:153-171; 201-224.

Nemiah, J. C. (1961), *Foundations of Psychopathology*. New York: Oxford University Press.

Noyes, A. P. & Kolb, L. C. (1968), *Modern Clinical Psychiatry*, 6th ed. Philadelphia & London: Saunders.

Reiser, M. F. (1966), Toward an Integrated Psychoanalytic-Physiological Theory of Psychosomatic Disorders. In: *Psychoanalysis—A General Psychology: Essays in Honor of Heinz Hartmann*, edited by R. M. Loewenstein, L. M. Newman, M. Schur, & A. J. Solnit. New York: International Universities Press, pp. 570-582.

Rosenbaum, M., Jacobs, T., & Oxenhorn, S. (1968), Issues Raised in Teaching Psychological Medicine to Medical Students, Medical Residents, and Family Physicians. In: *The Teaching of Dynamic Psychiatry*, edited by Grete L. Bibring. New York: International Universities Press, pp. 226-246.

Solnit, A. J. (1968), Eight Pediatricians and a Child Psychiatrist: A Study in Collaboration. In: *The Teaching of Dynamic Psychiatry*, edited by Grete L. Bibring. New York: International Universities Press, pp. 158-174.

Spock, B. (1946 and 1957), *The Common Sense Book of Baby and Child Care*. New York: Duell, Sloan & Pearce.

Waelder, R. (1960), *Basic Theory of Psychoanalysis*. New York: International Universities Press.

Wermer, H. and Stock, M. (1968), "I Am Just a Pediatrician": Educating Pediatricians in Dynamic Psychiatry. In: *The Teaching of Dynamic Psychiatry*, edited by Grete L. Bibring. New York: International Universities Press, pp. 143-157.

Zinberg, N. E., editor (1964), *Psychiatry and Medical Practice in a General Hospital*. New York: International Universities Press. Papers on the derivation, teaching, and some community applications of medical psychology.

Bibliography

Abraham, K., (1921), Contributions to the Theory of the Anal Character. In: *Selected Papers on Psychoanalysis*, 1:370-392. New York: Basic Books, 1954.

——— (1924), The Influence of Oral Erotism on Character Formation. In: *Selected Papers on Psychoanalysis*, 1:393-406. New York: Basic Books, 1954.

——— (1925), Character Formation on the Genital Level of Libido Development. In: *Selected Papers on Psychoanalysis*, 1:407-417. New York: Basic Books, 1954.

Aichhorn, A. (1925), *Wayward Youth*. New York: Viking Press, 1935.

Alexander, F. (1950), *Psychosomatic Medicine*. New York: Norton.

Amacher, P. (1965), *Freud's Neurological Education and Its Influence on Psychoanalytic Theory* [*Psychological Issues*, Monogr. 16]. New York: International Universities Press.

Arieti, S., ed. (1959, 1966), *American Handbook of Psychiatry*, 3 Volumes. New York: Basic Books.

Bakwin, H. (1942), Loneliness in Infants. *American Journal of the Diseases of Children*, 63:30-40.

——— (1949), Emotional Deprivation in Infants. *Journal of Pediatrics*, 35:512-521.

Balint, M. (1957), *The Doctor, His Patient, and the Illness*. New York: International Universities Press.

Beck, L. F. (1952), Unconscious Motivation. In: *Problems of Consciousness,* ed. H. A. Abramson, New York: Josiah Macy, Jr. Foundation, pp. 88-89.

Bellak, L., ed. (1952), *Psychology of Physical Illness.* New York: Grune & Stratton.

Bender, L. (1947), Childhood Schizophrenia. *American Journal of Orthopsychiatry,* 17:40-56.

———— & Yarnell, H. (1941), An Observational Nursery: A Study of 250 Children in the Psychiatric Division of Bellevue Hospital. *American Journal of Psychiatry,* 97:1158-1174.

Benedek, T. (1950), The Climacterium: A Developmental Phase. *Psychoanalytic Quarterly,* 19:1-27.

———— & Rubenstein, B. B. (1952), *Psychosexual Functions in Women.* New York: Ronald Press.

Beres, D. & Obers, S. J. (1950), The Effects of Extreme Deprivation in Infancy on Psychic Structure in Adolescence. *The Psychoanalytic Study of the Child,* 5:212-235. New York: International Universities Press.

Bergman, P. & Escalona. S. K. (1949), Unusual Sensitivities in Very Young Children. *The Psychoanalytic Study of the Child,* 3/4:333-352. New York: International Universities Press.

Bergmann, T. (1937), Versuch der Behebung einer Erziehungsschwierigkeit [An Attempt at Correcting a Learning Difficulty]. *Zeitschrift für psychoanalytische Pädogogik,* 11:29-43.

———— & Freud, A. (1965), *Children in the Hospital.* New York: International Universities Press.

Berliner, B. (1947), On Some Psychodynamics of Masochism. *Psychoanalytic Quarterly,* 16:459-471.

Betlheim, S. & Hartmann, H. (1924), On Parapraxes in the Korsakoff Psychosis. In: *Essays on Ego Psychology,* by H. Hartmann. New York: International Universities Press, 1964, pp. 353-368.

Bibring, E. (1953), The Mechanism of Depression. In: *Affective Disorders,* ed. P. Greenacre. New York: International Universities Press, pp. 13-48.

———— (1954), Psychoanalysis and the Dynamic Psychotherapies.

Journal of the American Psychoanalytic Association, 2:745-770.

Bibring, G. L. (1940), Über eine orale Komponente bei männlicher Inversion [On an Oral Component in Masculine Inversion]. *Internationale Zeitschrift für Psychoanalyse und Imago*, 25:124-130.

——— (1947), Psychiatry and Social Work. *Journal of Social Casework*, 28:203-211.

——— (1949), Psychiatric Principles in Casework. *Journal of Social Casework*, 30:230-235.

——— (1953), On the "Passing of the Oedipus Complex" in a Matriarchal Family Setting. In: *Drives, Affects, Behavior*, ed. R. M. Loewenstein. New York: International Universities Press, pp. 278-284.

——— (1956), Psychiatry and Medical Practice in a General Hospital. *New England Journal of Medicine*, 254:366-372.

——— (1959), Some Considerations of the Psychological Processes in Pregnancy. *The Psychoanalytic Study of the Child*, 14:113-127. New York: International Universities Press.

——— (1966), Old Age: Its Liabilities and Its Assets: A Psychobiological Discourse. In: *Psychoanalysis—A General Psychology: Essays in Honor of Heinz Hartmann*, ed. R. M. Loewenstein, L. M. Newman, M. Schur, & A. J. Solnit. New York: International Universities Press, pp. 253-271.

——— ed. (1968), *The Teaching of Dynamic Psychiatry*. New York: International Universities Press.

——— Dwyer, T. F., Huntington, D. S., & Valenstein, A. F. (1961), A Study of the Psychological Processes in Pregnancy and the Earliest Mother-Child Relationship. *The Psychoanalytic Study of the Child*, 16:9-72. New York: International Universities Press.

Binger, C. (1945), *The Doctor's Job*. New York: Norton.

Bird, B. (1955), *Talking with Patients*. Philadelphia: Lippincott.

Birren, J. E., ed. (1959), *Handbook of Aging and the Individual*. Chicago: University of Chicago Press.

Blos, P. (1962), *On Adolescence*. New York: Free Press of Glencoe.

Bonnard, A., Frankl, L., & Robinson, B. (1949), Children without Roots. *New Era* (London), 30:96-101.

Bornstein, B. (1951), On Latency. *The Psychoanalytic Study of the Child*, 6:279-285. New York: International Universities Press.

Bowlby, J. (1951), *Maternal Care and Mental Health*. Geneva: World Health Organization.

——— Robertson, J., & Rosenbluth, D. (1952), A Two-year-old Goes to Hospital. *The Psychoanalytic Study of the Child*, 7:82-94. New York: International Universities Press.

Brenner, C. (1955), *An Elementary Textbook of Psychoanalysis*. New York: International Universities Press.

Breuer, J. & Freud, S. (1893-1895), Studies on Hysteria. *Standard Edition*, 2. London: Hogarth Press, 1955.

Busse, E. W. (1959), Psychopathology. In: *Handbook of Aging and the Individual*, ed. J. E. Birren. Chicago: University of Chicago Press, pp. 364-399.

Chandler, A. R. (1949), The Traditional Chinese Attitude towards Old Age. *Journal of Gerontology*, 4:239-244.

Clyne, M. B. (1961), *Night Calls: A Study in General Practice*. London: Tavistock Publications.

Comfort, A. (1956), *The Biology of Senescence*. New York: Rinehart.

Deutsch, F. (1939), The Choice of Organ in Organ Neurosis. *International Journal of Psycho-Analysis*, 20:252-262.

Deutsch, H. (1944-1945), *The Psychology of Women*, 2 Volumes. New York: Grune & Stratton.

——— (1967), *Selected Problems of Adolescence*. New York: International Universities Press.

Dwyer, T. F. (1968), Psychoanalytic Teaching in the Medical School. In: *The Teaching of Dynamic Psychiatry*, ed. G. L. Bibring. New York: International Universities Press, pp. 23-37.

Easser, B. R. & Lesser, S. R. (1965), Hysterical Personality: A Re-evaluation. *Psychoanalytic Quarterly*, 34:390-405.

Eissler, K. R. (1955), *The Psychiatrist and the Dying Patient*. New York: International Universities Press.

Engel, G. L. (1955), Studies of Ulcerative Colitis: III. The Nature of the Psychologic Process. *American Journal of Medicine*, 19:231-256.

—— (1962), *Psychological Development in Health and Disease.* Philadelphia: Saunders.

Erikson, E. H. (1950), *Childhood and Society.* New York: Norton.

—— (1958), The Nature of Clinical Evidence. In: *Evidence and Inference,* ed. D. Lerner. Glencoe, Ill.: Free Press, pp. 73-95.

—— (1959), *Identity and the Life Cycle* [*Psychological Issues,* Monogr. 1]. New York: International Universities Press.

Ewalt, J. R. & Farnsworth, D. L. (1963), *A Textbook of Psychiatry.* New York: McGraw-Hill.

Fish, B. (1959), Longitudinal Observations of Biological Deviations in a Schizophrenic Infant. *American Journal of Psychiatry,* 116:25-31.

Fraiberg, S. (1959), *The Magic Years.* New York: Scribner's.

Freud, A. (1936), *The Ego and the Mechanisms of Defense.* New York: International Universities Press, rev. ed., 1966.

—— (1952), The Role of Bodily Illness in the Mental Life of Children. *The Psychoanalytic Study of the Child,* 7:69-81. New York: International Universities Press.

—— (1958), Adolescence. *The Psychoanalytic Study of the Child,* 13:255-278. New York: International Universities Press.

—— (1965), *Normality and Pathology in Childhood: Assessments of Development.* New York: International Universities Press.

—— & Burlingham, D. T. (1942), *War and Children.* New York: International Universities Press, 1943.

—— —— (1943), *Infants Without Families.* New York: International Universities Press, 1944.

Freud, S. (1897), Letters to Wilhelm Fliess, Letter No. 69. *Standard Edition,* 1:259-260. London: Hogarth Press, 1966.

—— (1900), The Interpretation of Dreams. *Standard Edition,* 4 & 5. London: Hogarth Press, 1953.

—— (1905a), Fragment of an Analysis of a Case of Hysteria. *Standard Edition,* 7:3-122. London: Hogarth Press, 1953.

—— (1905b), Three Essays on the Theory of Sexuality. *Standard Edition,* 7:123-243. London: Hogarth Press, 1953.

—————— (1908), Character and Anal Erotism. *Standard Edition*, 9:167-175. London: Hogarth Press, 1959.

—————— (1910), Five Lectures on Psycho-Analysis. *Standard Edition*, 11:3-55. London: Hogarth Press, 1957.

—————— (1913), Totem and Taboo. *Standard Edition*, 13:1-161. London: Hogarth Press, 1955.

—————— (1916-1917), Introductory Lectures on Psycho-Analysis. *Standard Edition*, 15 & 16. London: Hogarth Press, 1963.

—————— (1917), Mourning and Melancholia. *Standard Edition*, 14:237-258. London: Hogarth Press, 1957.

—————— (1924), The Dissolution of the Oedipus Complex. *Standard Edition*, 19:173-179. London: Hogarth Press, 1961.

—————— (1932), My Contact with Josef Popper-Lynkeus. *Standard Edition*, 22:219-224. London: Hogarth Press, 1964.

—————— (1933), New Introductory Lectures on Psycho-Analysis. *Standard Edition*, 22:3-182. London: Hogarth Press, 1964.

Friedlander, K. (1942), Children's Books and Their Function in Latency and Prepuberty. *American Imago*, 3:129-150.

Gill, M. M., Newman, R., & Redlich, F. C. (1954), *The Initial Interview in Psychiatric Practice*. New York: International Universities Press.

Gitelson, M. (1958), On Ego Distortion. *International Journal of Psycho-Analysis*, 39:245-257.

Goldfarb, A. I. (1956), Psychotherapy of the Aged. *Psychoanalytic Review*, 43:68-81.

Goldfarb, W. (1945), Effects of Psychological Deprivation in Infancy and Subsequent Stimulation. *American Journal of Psychiatry*, 102:18-33.

—————— & Dorsen, M. M. (1956), *Annotated Bibliography of Childhood Schizophrenia and Related Disorders*. New York: Basic Books.

Grinstein, A. (1956-1966), *The Index of Psychoanalytic Writings*, 9 Volumes. New York: International Universities Press.

Harlow, H. F. (1958), The Nature of Love. *American Psychologist*, 13:673-685.

—————— (1961), The Development of the Affectional Patterns in Infant Monkeys. In: *Determinants of Infant Behavior*, ed. B. M. Foss. New York: Wiley, pp. 75-88.

————— (1962), The Heterosexual Affectional System in Monkeys. *American Psychologist*, 17:1-9.

Hartmann, H. (1939), *Ego Psychology and the Problem of Adaptation*. New York: International Universities Press, 1958.

————— (1958), Comments on the Scientific Aspects of Psychoanalysis. *The Psychoanalytic Study of the Child*, 13:127-146. New York: International Universities Press.

————— (1964), *Essays on Ego Psychology*. New York: International Universities Press.

————— & Kris, E. (1945), The Genetic Approach in Psychoanalysis. *The Psychoanalytic Study of the Child*, 1:11-30. New York: International Universities Press.

Henderson, D., Gillespie, R. D., & Batchelor, I. R. C. (1962), *A Textbook of Psychiatry for Students and Practitioners*, 9th ed. New York: Oxford University Press.

Hendrick, I. (1958), *Facts and Theories of Psychoanalysis*, 3rd ed. New York: Knopf.

Hinsie, L. E. & Campbell, R. J. (1960), *Psychiatric Dictionary*, 3rd ed. New York: Oxford University Press.

Hinton, J. (1967), *Dying*. Baltimore: Penguin Books.

Horney, K. (1937), *The Neurotic Personality of Our Time*. New York: Norton.

Jessner, L. & Kaplan, S. (1949), Observations on the Emotional Reactions of Children to Tonsillectomy and Adenoidectomy. In: *Problems of Infancy and Childhood* [*Transactions of the Third Conference*], ed. M. J. E. Senn. New York: Josiah Macy, Jr. Foundation, 1949, pp. 97-117.

Jones, E. (1916), The God Complex. In: *Essays in Applied Psycho-Analysis*, 2:244-265. New York: International Universities Press, 1964.

————— (1953-1957), *The Life and Work of Sigmund Freud*, 3 Volumes. New York: Basic Books.

Kahana, R. J. (1967), Medical Management, Psychotherapy, and Aging. *Journal of Geriatric Psychiatry*, 1:78-89.

————— & Bibring, G. L. (1964), Personality Types in Medical Management. In: *Psychiatry and Medical Practice in a General Hospital*, ed. N. E. Zinberg. New York: International Universities Press, pp. 108-123.

Kallman, F. J. (1953), *Heredity in Health and Mental Disorders.* New York: Norton.

Kanner, L. (1942-1943), Autistic Disturbance of Affective Contact. *Nervous Child*, 2:217-250.

Kaplan, A. (1964), *The Conduct of Inquiry.* San Francisco: Chandler Publishing Co.

Kaufman, M. R., ed. (1965), *The Psychiatric Unit in a General Hospital.* New York: International Universities Press.

—— Franzblau, A. N., & Kairys, D. (1956), The Emotional Impact of Ward Rounds. *Journal of Mount Sinai Hospital*, 23:782-803.

Knight, R. P. (1949), A Critique of the Present Status of the Psychotherapies. *Bulletin of the New York Academy of Medicine*, 25:100-114.

—— (1953), Borderline States. *Bulletin of the Menninger Clinic*, 17:1-12.

Kris, E. (1947), The Nature of Psychoanalytic Propositions and Their Validation. In: *Psychological Theory*, ed. M. H. Marx. New York: Macmillan, 1951, pp. 332-351.

Levin, S. (1965), Some Suggestions for Treating the Depressed Patient. *Psychoanalytic Quarterly*, 34:37-65.

Levine, M. (1942), *Psychotherapy in Medical Practice.* New York: Macmillan.

Lidz, T., Fleck, S., & Cornelison, A. R. (1965), *Schizophrenia and the Family.* New York: International Universities Press.

Lindemann, E. & Dawes, L. G. (1952), The Use of Psychoanalytic Constructs in Preventive Psychiatry. *The Psychoanalytic Study of the Child*, 7:429-448. New York: International Universities Press.

Linn, L., ed. (1961), *Frontiers in General Hospital Psychiatry.* New York: International Universities Press.

Lipowski, Z. J. (1967), Review of Consultation Psychiatry and Psychosomatic Medicine. *Psychosomatic Medicine*, 29:153-171; 201-224.

Lorge, I. (1939), Psychometry: The Evaluation of Mental Status as a Function of the Mental Test. [In: Section Meetings on Old Age and Aging: The Present Status of Scientific Knowledge.] *American Journal of Orthopsychiatry*, 10:56-57.

McDougall, W. (1908), *An Introduction to Social Psychology*. Boston: John W. Luce & Co., 14th edition, 1921.

Mahler, M. S. (1952), On Child Psychosis and Schizophrenia: Autistic and Symbiotic Infantile Psychoses. *The Psychoanalytic Study of the Child*, 7:286-305. New York: International Universities Press.

Mendelson, M. (1960), *Psychoanalytic Concepts of Depression*. Springfield, Ill.: Charles C Thomas.

Mesmer, F. A. (1779), Dissertation on the Discovery of Animal Magnetism. In: *Mesmerism*, with an introductory monograph by Gilbert Frankau. London: Macdonald, 1948.

Milne, A. A. (1924), *When We Were Very Young*. New York: Dutton, 1952.

Mirsky, I. A. (1958), Physiologic, Psychologic and Social Determinants in the Etiology of Duodenal Ulcer. *American Journal of Digestive Diseases*, 3:285-314.

Nachmansohn, M. (1925), Concerning Experimentally Produced Dreams. In: *Organization and Pathology of Thought*, ed. D. Rapaport. New York: Columbia University Press, 1951, pp. 257-287.

Nemiah, J. C. (1961), *Foundations of Psychopathology*. New York: Oxford University Press.

Noyes, A. P. & Kolb, L. C. (1968), *Modern Clinical Psychiatry*. Philadelphia & London: Saunders, 6th edition.

Pasternak, B. (1931), *Safe Conduct*. New York: Signet Books, 1959.

Payne, E. C., Jr. (1967), The Physician and the Patient Who Is Dying. In: *Psychodynamic Studies on Aging: Creativity, Reminiscing, and Dying*, ed. S. Levin & R. J. Kahana. New York: International Universities Press, pp. 111-163.

Pearson, G. H. J. & English, O. S. (1937), *Common Neuroses of Children and Adults*. New York: Norton.

Pinner, M. & Miller, B. F. (1952), *When Doctors Are Patients*. New York: Norton.

Pötzl, O., Allers, R. & Teler, J. (1917, 1924), *Preconscious Stimulation in Dreams, Associations and Images* [*Psychological Issues*, Monogr. 7] New York: International Universities Press, 1960.

Prange, A. J., Jr. & Abse, D. W. (1957), Psychic Events Accompanying an Attack of Poliomyelitis. *British Journal of Medical Psychology*, 30:75-87.

Provence, S. & Lipton, R. C. (1962), *Infants in Institutions*. New York: International Universities Press.

———— & Ritvo, S. (1961), Effects of Deprivation on Institutionalized Infants: Disturbances in Development of Relationships to Inanimate Objects. *The Psychoanalytic Study of the Child*, 16:189-205. New York: International Universities Press.

Pumpian-Mindlin, E., ed. (1952), *Psychoanalysis As Science*. Stanford: Stanford University Press.

Rank, B. (1949), Adaptation of the Psychoanalytic Technique for the Treatment of Young Children with Atypical Development. *American Journal of Orthopsychiatry*, 19:130-139.

Reiser, M. F. (1966), Toward an Integrated Psychoanalytic-Physiological Theory of Psychosomatic Disorders. In: *Psychoanalysis—A General Psychology: Essays in Honor of Heinz Hartmann*, ed. R. M. Loewenstein, L. M. Newman, M. Schur, & A. J. Solnit. New York: International Universities Press, pp. 570-582.

Roffenstein, G. (1924), Experiments on Symbolization in Dreams. In: *Organization and Pathology of Thought*, ed. D. Rapaport. New York: Columbia University Press, 1951, pp. 249-256.

Rosenbaum, M., Jacobs, T., & Oxenhorn, S. (1968), Issues Raised in Teaching Psychological Medicine to Medical Students, Medical Residents, and Family Physicians. In: *The Teaching of Dynamic Psychiatry*, ed. G. L. Bibring. New York: International Universities Press, pp. 226-246.

Schroetter, K. (1911), Experimental Dreams. In: *Organization and Pathology of Thought*, ed. D. Rapaport. New York: Columbia University Press, 1951, pp. 234-248.

Simmons, L. W. (1946), Attitudes toward Aging and the Aged in Primitive Societies. *Journal of Gerontology*, 1:72-95.

Solnit, A. J. (1960), Hospitalization: An Aid to Physical and Psychological Health in Childhood. *A.M.A. Journal of the Diseases of Childhood*, 99:155-163.

———— (1968), Eight Pediatricians and a Child Psychiatrist: A Study in Collaboration. In: *The Teaching of Dynamic Psy-*

chiatry, ed. G. L. Bibring. New York: International Universities Press, pp. 158-174.

Spitz, R. A. (1945), Hospitalism: An Inquiry into the Genesis of Psychiatric Conditions in Early Childhood. *The Psychoanalytic Study of the Child*, 1:53-74. New York: International Universities Press.

———— (1946), Hospitalism: A Follow-up Report. *The Psychoanalytic Study of the Child*, 2:113-117. New York: International Universities Press.

———— & Wolf, K. M. (1946), Anaclitic Depression: An Inquiry into the Genesis of Psychiatric Conditions in Early Childhood. *The Psychoanalytic Study of the Child*, 2:313-342. New York: International Universities Press.

Spock, B. (1946 and 1957), *The Common Sense Book of Baby and Child Care*. New York: Duell, Sloan & Pearce.

Stewart, W. A. (1967), *Psychoanalysis: The First Ten Years, 1888-1898*. New York: Macmillan.

Talbot, F. B. (1941), Transactions of the American Pediatric Society, 1941, discussion of paper by Bakwin. *American Journal of the Diseases of Children*, 62:469.

Titchener, J. L. & Levine, M. (1960), *Surgery As a Human Experience*. New York: Oxford University Press.

Von Mering, O. & Weniger, F. L. (1959), Social-Cultural Background of the Aging Individual. In: *Handbook of Aging and the Individual*, ed. J. E. Birren. Chicago: University of Chicago Press, pp. 279-335.

Waelder, R. (1960), *Basic Theory of Psychoanalysis*. New York: International Universities Press.

Welford, A. T. (1959), Psychomotor Performance. In: *Handbook of Aging and the Individual*, ed. J. E. Birren. Chicago: University of Chicago Press, pp. 562-613.

Wermer, H. & Stock, M. (1968), "I Am Just a Pediatrician": Educating Pediatricians in Dynamic Psychiatry. In: *The Teaching of Dynamic Psychiatry*, ed. G. L. Bibring. New York: International Universities Press, pp. 143-157.

Whitehorn, J. C. (1944), Guide to Interviewing and Clinical Personality Study. *Archives of Neurology and Psychiatry*, 52:197-216.

Winnicott, D. W. (1953), Transitional Objects and Transitional Phenomena. *International Journal of Psycho-Analysis*, 34:1-9.

Yeats, W. B. (1927), Sailing to Byzantium. In: *The Collected Poems of W. B. Yeats.* New York: Macmillan, 1933.

Zilboorg, G. & Henry, C. W. (1941), *A History of Medical Psychology.* New York: Norton.

Zinberg, N. E., ed. (1964), *Psychiatry and Medical Practice in a General Hospital.* New York: International Universities Press.

Zweig, S. (1932), *Mental Healers: Mesmer, Eddy and Freud.* Garden City: Garden City Publishing Co.

Index

8501